ELEMENTARY
MEDICAL
BIOCHEMISTRY

To
Our
Students

ELEMENTARY MEDICAL BIOCHEMISTRY

by

J. M. M. BROWN

D.V.Sc.(Pret.)

Professor in the Department of Physiology
University of Pretoria

and

G. G. JÁROS

Pr.Eng., M.Sc.(Eng.)(Wits.), D.Sc.(Pret.)

Senior lecturer in the Department of Physiology
University of Pretoria

DURBAN
BUTTERWORTHS
1977

THE BUTTERWORTH GROUP

South Africa
BUTTERWORTH & CO (SA) (PTY) LTD
152-154 Gale Street, Durban 4001

England
BUTTERWORTH & CO (PUBLISHERS) LTD
88 Kingsway, London, WC2B 6AB

Australia
BUTTERWORTHS PTY LTD
586 Pacific Highway, Chatswood, Sydney NSW 2067

Canada
BUTTERWORTH & CO (CANADA) LTD
2265 Midland Avenue, Scarborough, Ontario, M1P 4S1

New Zealand
BUTTERWORTHS OF NEW ZEALAND LTD
T & W Young Building, 77-85 Customhouse Quay, Wellington

USA
BUTTERWORTH PUBLISHERS INC
10 Tower Office Park, Woburn, MA 01801

Printed in South Africa by
INTERPRINT (PTY) LIMITED
DURBAN

iv

Foreword

This book has been written to comply with the requirements of students of nursing who are following diploma courses in General, Obstetric and Psychiatric Nursing.

The authors have long been involved in the teaching of biochemistry and physiology to nursing students. They are well aware that nurses are not interested in laboratory chemistry as such, but rather in the process of life, and they apply this principle in their approach to the teaching of this subject, by introducing the student step by step to the biochemical basis of the process of life.

The nursing profession has long felt the need for this kind of literature. This is an essential textbook, not only for students of basic nursing, but also for those who, wishing to follow advanced nursing courses, feel the need of revision. It will provide the basis for an understanding of more advanced work in this subject.

In order to foster in nurses an understanding of the biochemical basis of the health requirements of human beings, and thus to ensure better care for the sick in South Africa, the authors have devoted much valuable time to the preparation of this book.

CHARLOTTE SEARLE, D.PHIL., R.G.N., R.M.
Professor and Head of the Department of Nursing Science
University of South Africa

Pretoria 1977

Introduction

Courses in Biochemistry, or Physiological Chemistry as it is sometimes called, form part of practically all Medical and Paramedical syllabuses throughout the world. These courses are considered as being fundamental to disciplines such as Physiology, Pharmacology, Gynaecology, Anaesthesiology, Dietetics and Chemical Pathology, to name but a few. One of the greatest problems facing paramedical students is the fact that most of them have not been taught chemistry and physics during their high school years, and are therefore unable to follow the usual courses in Biochemistry. The language of chemistry, consisting of symbols, reactions and formulas is strange to them, presenting them with seemingly insurmountable obstacles. During the compilation of this book we have assumed that the knowledge of chemistry and physics of our students is very rudimentary. For this reason the text starts from the most basic principles and gradually leads up to a more complicated study of metabolic processes and of the systems controlling these processes. Although this approach might appear naïve at first glance, we have used it successfully in our courses for the last ten to fifteen years.

We trust that this book will also be found useful by those who have already been subjected to a formal Biochemistry course during their medical training, and who now intend to brush up on the basic principles underlying metabolic processes.

It has been said that books are written for the satisfaction of the reader or for the satisfaction of the author. With regard to the latter, it may be said with justification that sometimes in our enthusiasm we have been carried away. Since the publication of this book in Afrikaans last year, we have had a considerable volume of feedback from those who have had to use it, either in a tutorial or in a student role. This has resulted in a little more than just a straightforward translation of the work. Acting on numerous suggestions we have re-arranged the presentation of some of the material for this edition. A considerable amount of needless repetition has been eliminated. We have inserted many more subtitles in each chapter, which we hope will serve to delineate more clearly the important aspects of the material being discussed and facilitate the reading of it. We hope that in its present form this work will bring some greater measure of satisfaction to the reader.

We would like to thank sincerely those who have helped us. Mrs. H. Botha, Mrs. A. M. Brown and Mrs. C. M. Bornman spent many long hours typing the manuscript, Mrs. K. Járos and Mrs. R. Jordaan drew most of the diagrams. Figure 7.2 was drawn by Mr. L. van Heerden.

J. M. M. BROWN

G. G. JÁROS

Pretoria
September, 1976

Contents

Chapter 9 — The Digestion and Absorption of Nutrients

Chapter 10 — Metabolism

Chapter 11 — The Handling of End-products of Metabolism by the Body

CHAPTER 1

Matter and Energy

Biochemistry is the study of interactions or *reactions* that take place in biological systems between different types of matter. The phenomenon which we call *life* is the result of an integration of a very large number of biochemical reactions. The wonderful way in which reacting systems are organized within living cells to produce this integration is something which at once distinguishes living systems from chemical reactions performed in the laboratory.

Any reaction, whether it takes place in a living system or in a test tube, depends on the movement of the different reacting forms of matter. The movement or even the ability to cause movement is referred to as *energy*. Life can therefore be considered to result from the orderly and specific application of energy. During the course of this chapter we will become acquainted with the different forms and states of matter, with the two forms of energy, and with the significance of these for biological systems.

Elements and compounds

Everything that occupies space irrespective of whether it is large enough to be seen or not, is called *matter*. Any object, large or small, lifeless or living, consists thus of matter. This matter is built up out of subunits, viz, *atoms*, *ions* or *molecules*, that are so small that they cannot be seen even with the most advanced microscopes. From the behaviour of these subunits, we can predict their appearance and in many instances it is possible to construct meaningful models of them. In other words, even though we cannot see them, their *structure* is known to us. This state of affairs is by no means strange in science. Until a few years ago no one had seen a virus, yet we could predict the characteristics of viruses from the knowledge of the disease conditions which they caused. Now, thanks to the advent of advanced electron microscopes, the structure and appearance of viruses is well known and has generally proved to be what has been predicted.

All subunits are in turn composed of still smaller particles called *protons*, *electrons* and *neutrons*. The *atom* consists of a *nucleus*, containing protons and neutrons, about which electrons move in *elliptical orbits* much like our planets moving around the sun. Protons are positively charged particles, whereas neutrons are electrically neutral but have the same size as protons. The electrons are much smaller in size and are negatively charged.[1] It is characteristic of atoms that the number of protons in the nucleus is always equal to the number of electrons in the orbits. This means that the positive and negative charges cancel each other out and an atom consequently is electrically neutral. The simplest atom in nature is the hydrogen atom, which consists of one proton and no neutron in the nucleus, and one electron in the orbit around it. The oxygen atom contains 8 protons, 8 neutrons and 8 electrons; the nitrogen atom has seven of each. However it does not necessarily follow that the number of protons must equal the number of neutrons. For example we have seen that the hydrogen atom has one proton but no neutrons. In the case of many atoms, closely related forms called *isotopes* can be produced by varying the number of neutrons while keeping the number of protons constant.

Ions are basically similar to atoms except that the number of electrons does not equal the number of protons. They can be considered as atoms from which electrons have been removed or to which electrons have been added. This results in them carrying a positive or negative charge as opposed to the atom which carries no charge. Positive ions are referred to as *cations*, because in an electrical field they move to the negative electrode (Gr. kata[2] = down; negative being considered as down). Negative ions are called *anions* (Gr. ana = up). *Molecules* are formed when two or more atoms or ions combine with one another. The atoms or ions which enter into combination may be of the same or of a different kind.

When a certain form of matter is built up from the same subunits it is called a *substance*. One of the best known substances is water: irrespective of how small the quantities are that we take of it, these always remain in the form of water. Iron, copper, hydrochloric acid and ammonia are further examples of well known substances. We can reduce iron or copper to a fine powder without changing them into something else. Substances such as these fall into two main groups, notably elements and compounds.

When a substance is composed of the same type of atoms, ions or molecules, it is called an *element*. Over a hundred elements are

---

[1] The mass of electrons is about 1 800 times smaller than that of the neutrons and protons. The absolute mass of protons is $1,672 \times 10^{-27}$kg and that of electrons is $0,9109 \times 10^{-30}$kg. They are therefore all very small indeed.

[2] The prefixes ana- and cata- are also used in two very important words of biology, viz, anabolism and catabolism, meaning building up and breaking down of large molecules, respectively.

known, of which only about seventy are found in nature; the rest can be produced artificially. Elements differ from one another according to the number of protons present in their nuclei. Hydrogen has one, oxygen eight, nitrogen seven and so on. *Compounds* are substances in which the subunits are molecules made up of two or more different atoms or ions. A water molecule consists for example of two hydrogen and one oxygen atom.

Energy: Life and movement

As has been mentioned earlier, the phenomenon that we call life consists of a large number of highly integrated and finely controlled series of chemical reactions. These reactions are dependant on the continuous movement of the subunits of matter, and on the resulting "collisions" made by these with one another. The ability of an object to move and to cause other objects to move is called the *energy* of the object. We can compare this concept with the idea of people who are always on the move. We say that such persons have lots of "energy" and we know that they can move about and are able to perform useful work. We know also, that if the energetic activities of anyone are performed in a disorganized fashion, this can lead to a chaotic waste of time and energy. Such persons may in the extreme event even pose a problem to the organized life around them.

All bodily movements, for instance those of muscles, of the heart, of the blood within the blood vessels, the to and fro movement of air in the respiratory passages and so on are dependant on energy. These processes proceed continuously without our generally being aware of them. Sometimes however when we suddenly resume activity after a period of rest, i.e. when we suddenly start using more energy, we become aware of our heart beats, respiration and a marked production of body heat.

We generally speak of two kinds of energy, viz, *potential* and *kinetic* energy. The former is a stored form of energy that can be released to cause movement (Latin, potens = ability). The second form is energy due to the movement of objects (Greek, kineo = to move). We can best illustrate the meaning of these concepts with simple commonplace examples. Consider for example two boys pulling on a rope. If both have the same physical strength neither of them will be moved from his position. If both are pulling hard there will be a great deal of tension in the rope and thus in the system consisting of the rope and the two boys. If someone suddenly cuts the rope or it breaks of its own accord, then the two boys will fall in opposite directions. The system is said to have potential energy which can be released as kinetic energy when the rope is cut. The boys who now move in opposite directions can collide with bystanders and cause them to move as well. The two boys thus now have kinetic energy.

Another example which can serve to illustrate the point further, is a game of marbles. Before the large marble is played, potential energy develops in the fingers of the player. When the large marble is shot, it possesses kinetic energy as it moves through the air. As it strikes the other marbles, it causes them to fly out in different directions, thus indicating that part of the kinetic energy has been transferred to them.

In biological systems the subunits of matter are held together by *chemical bonds*. These bonds can be compared with the rope held by the two boys in our previous example. When a bond is formed a certain quantity of energy is built into the compound concerned. In other words, the kinetic energy causing the units to "collide" with one another is converted into potential energy. When a chemical bond is broken this energy can be released once more and be converted into kinetic energy that manifests itself in the movement of the free subunits.

We can borrow a further example from everyday life to illustrate the way in which the conversion of kinetic to potential energy can influence the combination of two subunits. Let us suppose that a certain boy X lives in a particular town, and that a girl Y lives in another town. They do not know one another nor will they have a chance to do so if they do not move out of their respective towns. Once they do so, the chances of meeting somewhere improve considerably. They might perhaps go to the same holiday resort one day and meet one another there. Should they find each other attractive, their meeting could lead to a firm relationship. By the same token, the creation of a chemical bond depends upon the necessary movement of the subunits concerned and the forces of attraction that will hold them together.

The energy present in biological systems is mainly the result of the reaction between *oxygen* (which is inhaled) and *hydrogen* (which is present in the food that we eat, and which is stored in our tissue cells). This reaction and the series of reactions leading to it take place in the tissue cells and like all other reactions in the body, in a well controlled and integrated manner. There might be a whole series of potential-kinetic energy interconversions before the final form of energy is produced.

Our food, which contains hydrogen atoms attached to other constituents by a great variety of chemical bonds, can be regarded as a *store of energy*. The fuel in the petrol tank of a car can be considered to be the same form of potential energy. To release this energy the fuel is brought into contact with oxygen and ignited. This requires an additional, but relatively small quantity of energy supplied in the form of a spark supplied from the battery of the car. The process of *combustion* is initiated or activated in much the same way as the potential energy was released when the rope pulled by the two boys was cut. In the body combustion of our food is activated by *enzymes*. These will be discussed at length in some of the later chapters.

A certain amount of the energy obtained from our foods (about 45%) is stored in the form of the chemical compound *adenosine triphosphate* (ATP). This energy can be released and used when it is required for the various physiological functions of the body. The remaining 55% of energy produced is released in the body as *heat*. Some of this heat is used to maintain body temperature; the rest is lost to the surroundings.

It should be apparent from the present discussion that energy plays a central role in living systems. A large part of this book is devoted to the involved way in which this energy is finally produced and utilized.

The states of matter

The subunits of matter undergo a continuous state of movement. The rate at which this occurs is indicated by the *temperature* of the matter in question. There are three states of matter, notably, *solid*, *liquid* and *gaseous* depending upon the rate of movement of the subunits concerned, and thus upon the temperature of the matter. Water, for example, can exist in the form of ice, liquid and vapour. At temperatures below about 0°C the rate of molecular movement in ice is low, and the molecules stay in positions which are relatively fixed with respect to one another. When the temperature is raised by addition of energy to the system, the molecules begin to move faster, the ice melts and water as we know it is formed. The molecules in this case are capable of moving away from each other but are unable to leave the volume of the liquid. We say that a liquid can change form but not volume. A further increase in the temperature increases the energy of some of the molecules to such an extent that they are capable of escaping from the main body of the liquid. These molecules form a gas or vapour wherein they tend to repel one another rather than exercise a force of attraction. Gas has neither definitive form nor volume, and the molecules move at tremendous speeds. Because of their excessive kinetic energy, gas molecules are much more reactive than those of solids and liquids. In some cases the change from one state to the other is so violent that the molecules concerned become destroyed. This happens when some object burns. A *fire or flame* can be considered as an extremely high level of kinetic energy.

Temperature and heat

The *temperature* of an object is an indication of the average rate of molecular activity within the object. When an object feels "warm" it means that the average molecular activity in the object is higher than that in our hand. A part of the molecular activity in the object is transferred to the skin of our hand. The skin has special nerve endings, the so-called *receptors*, that are sensitive to the increase in such molecular activity. The nerve endings are therefore stimulated and they transmit the relevant impulses via their axons to the appropriate areas of the brain where the phenomenon is interpreted as "heat". On the other hand, when the average molecular activity in an object is less than that in the skin of the hand of a person touching it, part of the molecular activity of the skin will be transferred to the object. Special receptors will again transmit the appropriate impulses to the brain and the phenomenon will be interpreted as "cold". Since temperature reflects the average molecular activity it is independent of the size of the object concerned. For example, a drawing pin can be at the same temperature as a large lump of iron. Temperature can be measured by means of a *thermometer* in *degrees Celsius* (°C) or in the absolute units known as *kelvin* (*K*). Another quantity that we must consider in addition to temperature is *heat*. By contrast with temperature the heat contained in an object is dependent upon the size of the object. The heat in a drawing pin will be much less than the corresponding heat in a large lump of iron, even though they might be at the same temperature. This can be demonstrated by immersing them both in a waterbath that is held at a lower temperature than they are. The temperature of the water will increase much more in the case of the lump of iron, than in that of the drawing pin. Therefore the two things that determine the heat in an object are the temperature and the size of the object. The unit of heat is the *joule* (*J*). In order to give an indication of the size of this unit, it may be mentioned that about 4 180 joule (or in other words 4,18 kilojoule) is necessary to increase the temperature of one kilogram water by one degree Celsius (1°C).

Substances differ in the way that they respond to additions of heat energy if their molecular structures are different. In some cases relatively small amounts of heat can cause appreciable changes in molecular activity and therefore in temperature. In other cases considerably more energy is needed to cause the same effect. For example, while as has been mentioned, 4,18 kJ was necessary to change the temperature of 1kg water by 1°C, only about a tenth of this amount will be necessary to change the temperature of the same amount of copper by one degree Celsius. In order to compare substances with one another in this regard we make use of a quantity known as the *specific heat capacity*. This can be defined as the heat needed to change the temperature of 1kg of the substance by 1°C. The units of specific heat capacity are joule/kilogram/°C (J/kg/°C). The specific heat of water is 4,18 kJ/kg/°C. The higher the specific heat of a substance, the more heat it can absorb or lose without an appreciable change of its temperature. This phenomenon is extremely important in biological systems in which the temperature must be maintained within narrow limits. The advantages of having about two-thirds of the body mass as water should be apparent to the reader.

Molecular transport processes in the body

The human body consists of a large number of substances mixed with or dissolved in the basic constituent, which is water. These substances as well as water can move about in the body by one of the following processes: diffusion, osmosis, filtration, active transport and circulation.

Diffusion occurs when the substances are present in *different concentrations* in various parts of the liquid. These substances then move from a higher to a lower concentration. An example of diffusion is the movement of oxygen and carbon dioxide in the lungs and in the tissues. In addition to this kind of diffusion ions can also diffuse as a result of *electrical forces*. For example, potassium ions (which carry a positive charge) move in and out of cells as a result of the influence of electrical forces, amongst other things.

Osmosis is also due to *concentration differences* but only occurs in cases when a *semipermeable membrane* is present between the areas of different concentration. The semipermeable membrane interferes with the diffusion process by prohibiting the passage of the dissolved substances. In order to cancel out the concentration differences the water in which the substances are dissolved moves through the membrane to the area of high substance concentration. An example of this is the reabsorption of water in the kidneys (chapter 5).

Filtration is the process by which the constituents of a mixture can be separated from each other by passing it through a *selectively permeable membrane*. Filtration of the blood occurs in the kidneys (chapter 5) and during this process the blood corpuscles and proteins are temporarily separated from other components of blood.

Active transport is a much more complicated type of mechanism by which various molecules can be moved through cell walls. It permits, for instance, the movement of ions *against* electrical *gradients*. For example a positive ion like the sodium ion can be moved to a positively charged area (chapter 3), instead of being repelled as one would expect. Molecules and ions can also be moved from low to high ion concentrations. For example, nutrients, such as glucose, fatty acids and amino acids are absorbed from the digestive tract by this mechanism (chapter 9). This is extremely important for the efficient utilisation of nutrients as these can be taken up even when their concentration in the digestive tract is smaller than in the rest of the body. Active transport occurs with the aid of *carriers* and *energy*. The carriers are usually specific types of proteins present in the cell membranes. The energy is obtained from the ATP produced by the cells concerned.

Active transport mechanisms are, in many instances, known to be regulated by *hormones*, which are the chemical messengers of the body. They are produced in the so-called endocrine glands and exercise their functions elsewhere in the body. We shall encounter these substances at various places in this book and they will also be summarized in chapter 12.

Circulation is movement of a liquid together with its dissolved constituents through *specific channels*. It includes thus the circulation of blood and lymph through their respective vessels.

CHAPTER 2

Oxygen, Hydrogen, Carbon and Nitrogen

The four most important elements found in biological systems are discussed in this chapter. In one sense, these elements can be considered to be of equal importance, since they are present in various combinations with one another in a multitude of cellular and tissue structures. In terms of what has been said in the previous chapter about the production of energy, oxygen is however of special *immediate* importance to the body. This is illustrated by the fact that it is impossible to live longer than a few minutes without breathing, but at the same time possible to exist for relatively long times without food. The air that we inhale contains oxygen and this combines with hydrogen in the tissues with the formation of energy. Oxygen is however not readily available from compounds present in the tissue, nor is it stored as such in the body for any appreciable length of time. The other elements which have been mentioned are on the other hand obtained from various large molecules present in the food. These large molecules are sequentially broken down through a series of intermediate products, some of which can be stored in the tissues of the body. It should be clear therefore why oxygen must be continuously inhaled, while the other elements need only be taken in intermittently, and then in the form of various compounds.

Oxygen (Symbol O)

The earth is surrounded by an atmosphere containing 21% oxygen. Life as we know it is impossible on the other planets that lack oxygen in their atmosphere. The oxygen is used for *oxidation* mainly within but also outside of living organisms. Oxidation can proceed at various rates ranging from the slow formation of rust in the case of iron, to violent explosions when gases are involved. Biological oxidations comprise mainly the *combustion* of hydrogen to form energy and water.

Combustion is generally associated with destructive processes and at first glance it may be difficult to appreciate that combustion is the basis of life. This apparent paradox can be explained by the fact that while a destructive fire is usually uncontrolled, the process of combustion is *extremely well controlled* in biological systems. The control is exercised mainly by enzymes (see chapter 8) and for this reason the process is called *enzymatic oxidation*. In the cells, enzymatic oxidation takes place mainly in special structures known as *mitochondria*, which can therefore be regarded as the power-houses of the cells. As mentioned in chapter 1 the energy released during combustion is either stored as ATP or is liberated as heat. This ATP is subsequently used for physiological work such as secretion, excretion, impulse conduction, muscle contraction and so on. The heat which is liberated is mainly used for the maintenance of body temperature, or to put it another way, to provide kinetic energy for the multitude of chemical reactions.

Uptake and Transport of Oxygen in the Body

Lower forms of life have the ability to take up oxygen directly from their environment, but in the higher animals oxygen follows a circuitous route before it reaches the tissues of the body. In humans and the higher animals, oxygen is taken up in the lungs. Here the inspired air comes in close contact with the blood over a large exchange area, represented by the walls of an extremely large amount of small spherical compartments, the *alveoli*, each of which is well supplied by a capillary network of blood vessels. The close contact of the air with blood is made possible by the presence of only two thin membranes, notably the alveolar membrane and the capillary membrane which separate the blood from the air. Oxygen diffuses across these two membranes with ease as a result of its high solubility in the substance of the membranes. There is also a difference in oxygen pressure between the two compartments concerned. In the case of a mixture of gasses the pressure exerted by each constituent is called the *partial pressure* and it is proportional to the percentage of the particular gas in the mixture. The partial pressure of oxygen, which constitutes 21% of atmospheric air, can be calculated as follows:

Total atmospheric pressure at sea level = 760mm Hg.[1]
Partial pressure is 21% of total = 160mm Hg.

Similarly one can calculate the partial pressure of oxygen in the alveoli. In this case, however, because of the carbon dioxide that is produced by the body and water vapour present in alveolar air, the amount of oxygen present is only about 13%. Therefore the partial pressure is 13% of 760 = 100mm Hg. The blood that enters the lungs comes from the tissues that have been extracting oxygen from it, and for this reason the partial pressure in this case is only 40mm Hg. It is this difference of pressure (100 − 40 = 60mm Hg.) that enables the diffusion of oxygen from the alveoli to the blood.

---

[1] Hg is the chemical symbol for the element, mercury (Hg is from the Latin for mercury, Hydrargyrum).

The *haemoglobin* present in the red blood cells takes up most of the oxygen reaching the blood. These cells then transport it to the tissues and release it for cellular use. The way in which oxygen binds with haemoglobin is a process different from oxidation and is known as *oxygenation*. The difference is that while oxidation is a stable or permanent association of oxygen with various elements, oxygenation is a readily reversible process. This reversibility is based on a loose association of oxygen with haemoglobin and is also regulated by the partial pressure of oxygen in the blood. As oxygen diffuses from the alveoli of the lungs into the blood the partial pressure of oxygen in the blood increases until it equals that in the alveoli, viz, 100mm Hg. This pressure causes the red blood cells to become saturated with oxygen. Under normal circumstances every 100ml blood leaving the lungs carries about 20ml oxygen. When the blood reaches the tissues it enters an area of low partial pressure of oxygen due to the previous utilisation of this compound by the tissue cells. This causes the haemoglobin to release part of its oxygen, normally about 5ml of the total carried by every 100ml blood. When more oxygen is needed, e.g. with increased activity in the tissues, more oxygen (up to 15ml/ 100ml) can be extracted from the haemoglobin.

The efficiency by which oxygen can be delivered to the tissues depends to a large extent on the efficiency of uptake as well as on the proper functioning of the transport system. Sufficient red blood cells must be present and sufficient blood must also circulate between the lungs and the tissues. The latter depends on the integrity and efficient function of the heart and blood vessels. As the main function of the circulation is to supply the tissues with sufficient oxygen, it must respond to the needs of tissues in this respect. This is indeed the case, since when certain tissues need more oxygen the blood circulation through them increases automatically. The processes that play a role in this regulation of circulation on the tissue level are called *autoregulatory processes*. There are also other ways in which the oxygen supply to tissues can be increased, e.g. by increased activity of the heart, reduced resistance against flow in the blood vessels, an increase in number of circulating cells, and so on.

All tissues have certain minimum requirements for oxygen, and when these are not met one speaks of *hypoxia* (low oxygen content) or *anoxia* (total absence of oxygen). These conditions can cause serious malfunction of tissues and even cellular death. Brain and heart tissue are especially vulnerable to hypoxia. If the blood flow to the heart is reduced, as in cases of coronary thrombosis, large parts of the heart muscle can become non-functional and this can result in the death of the individual. When an area in the brain is affected, as is the case in a stroke, there is generally a loss of one or more bodily functions which are regulated by the area of the brain affected.

As mentioned earlier the path that oxygen must follow to reach the tissues is an involved one. In the tissues themselves there are further pathways to and within the mitochondria where the final oxidation of energy yielding substances takes place. Any abnormality along the entire utilization pathway will result in an insufficient supply of oxygen to the energy producing systems within the cells, i.e. an hypoxia. For example there may be an insufficient uptake of oxygen by the arterial blood as the result of pneumonia, asthma, oedema or emphysema of the lungs and so on, leading to an *arterial hypoxia*. When an individual has a deficiency of red blood cells, *anaemic hypoxia* develops. When the circulation of blood is impaired due to malfunction of the heart or the blood vessels, *circulatory hypoxia* can develop. Sometimes it happens that the tissues themselves are not capable of taking up oxygen, as for example in cyanide poisoning. The oxygen deficiency in this case is termed *histotoxic hypoxia*.

Other important facts about oxygen

Oxygen, like all other substances can exist in three states, according to the kinetic energy of its molecules. It is liquid below $-183°C$, a solid below $-218°C$ and a *colourless, tasteless and odourless gas* at ordinary temperatures.

Oxygen is one of the most abundant elements on earth and apart from its elemental form it can be found in thousands of compounds. It is present in a very high concentration in all biological material. Only very low forms of life, such as the bacteria which cause diseases like tetanus, botulism and anthrax, can live without oxygen. Such forms of life are called *anaerobic organisms* (an = without).

Apart from combustion in living tissue, there is a continuous oxidation of dead matter. The presence of oxygen in water serves as a *cleansing agent* preventing the growth of many harmful microorganisms, and retarding the process of stagnation, thus enabling useful forms of life to exist in water. Despite the fact that oxygen is used up constantly in these ways, the total amount of oxygen in the atmosphere remains unchanged. This implies that a constant production of oxygen must also take place. This is indeed the case and plants are largely responsible for this. The constant production of oxygen goes hand in hand with the simultaneous utilization of carbon dioxide, produced by animals. The entire process as it occurs in plants is called *photosynthesis* and it requires the energy supplied by sunlight. By means of photosynthesis the plant builds up its own food reserves and structure material out of water and carbon dioxide, whilst simultaneously releasing oxygen. Plants have thus also a cleansing effect on the atmosphere by removing carbon dioxide and replacing it with oxygen. Many plant tissues, which like all living matter, contain hydrogen and carbon atoms, are used as sources of energy by humans and animals. There exists thus a cycle between the atmosphere, plants and animals for the exchange of oxygen, which is referred to as the *oxygen cycle*.

Medical uses of oxygen

Patients suffering from certain types of hypoxia are often made to inspire air that is enriched with oxygen. Even pure oxygen is used in certain cases (oxygen therapy). Both of these methods increase the amount of oxygen diffusing into the blood from the lungs, that taken up by the red blood cells and that received by the tissues. The following are a few examples of cases in which the use of *oxygen therapy* is recommended:

(a) pneumonia, in which a part of the lungs becomes ineffective;

(b) abnormal respiration during and after operations under anaesthesia;

(c) in new-born babies where normal methods of initiating breathing have proved ineffective; and

(d) in premature babies with undeveloped respiratory systems.

These babies are usually placed in *incubators* in which the composition of the air, its temperature and its humidity, are all controlled.

In adults oxygen therapy is often applied by placing the patient in a tent in which the oxygen concentration of the air has been increased (*oxygen tent*). The air pressure can at the same time be increased to improve diffusion even further (*hyperbaric chamber*). For emergency use oxygen masks are generally resorted to, especially in ambulances, and in domiciled critically ill patients.

In all types of oxygen therapy, the oxygen used is supplied from an oxygen cylinder. In the cylinder the gas is under great pressure in order to accommodate sufficient quantities and to ensure quick release. *This makes the use of oxygen dangerous.* Should the released oxygen molecules come in contact with substances which burn easily, fire and even explosions may result. Oil is one of these substances and for this reason all oily rags should be kept away from the neighbourhood of oxygen cylinders.

Hydrogen (Symbol H)

Hydrogen, carbon and nitrogen together with oxygen, form *carbohydrates, fats* and *proteins* that in turn form part of the plant and animal tissues that make up our diet. These important substances will be discussed repeatedly in later chapters. It suffices to say here that they are gradually broken down in the body to smaller components, firstly in the alimentary canal and then later in the tissue cells. Some molecules are stripped of their hydrogen which then combines with oxygen to provide energy. The process of degradation of nutrients is referred to as *catabolism* (kata = down, like in cation). Some of the nutrient molecules are used to build up human and animal tissues. The processes involved here are called *anabolic processes* (ana = up, like in anion). The two types of process are collectively termed *metabolic* processes.

Hydrogen is part of the water molecule, and is therefore very abundant in nature. Water contributes between 50 - 70 per cent of the mass of human and animal tissues.

A very small, but nevertheless important percentage of hydrogen is present in the *ionic form* in the cells of tissues. In this form hydrogen is a most active element, and binds readily with other substances. For this reason the concentration of hydrogen ions in the body is of primary importance. The concept of hydrogen ion concentration and its regulation will be discussed in detail in chapters 5 and 11, respectively.

Carbon (Symbol C)

We are familiar with carbon in the forms of coal and graphite which are black amorphous (= formless) substances. We should not be misled by this appearance since carbon can also be present in a variety of other forms, viz, *allotropic* elements (Gr. allotropia = another way, another form). For example, diamonds are pure crystals of very hard carbon. Substances like sugars and starches both belong to the group of compounds called carbohydrates, which contain large amounts of carbon in their molecules. The same is true for substances like petrol, benzene and lubricating oils which belong to the group of compounds known as hydrocarbons, as well as for fats and proteins present in plant and animal tissues.

An important carbon compound produced by the body during metabolism is *carbon dioxide*.[2] We shall discuss this extremely import-ant substance frequently in the pages which follow, and again in detail in chapter 11. It is important to remember however that although it is generally considered to be a waste product, it has some very important functions, and some carbon dioxide is required for

---

[2] It should be stressed here that carbon dioxide is not a result of the direct oxidation of carbon atoms in the body, but rather the result of the breakdown of carbohydrates and fats in the metabolic pathways (chapter 10).

the regulation of breathing and of the flow of blood through the brain. It helps in maintaining the correct acidity of the body in general and of the stomach in particular, by taking part in the production of hydrochloric acid.

Nitrogen (Symbol N)

Unlike the other three elements discussed in the present chapter, the most important function of nitrogen in nitrogenous (nitrogen containing) compounds is not in producing energy but rather in the construction of *tissue components*. Also while the other three are present in all of our foods in varying proportions, nitrogen is generally restricted to compounds like *proteins* and other specialized compounds. When we think of structure or components, walls, buildings, bridges, and other lifeless solid unchangeable materials, often come to mind. We even tend to consider our own skeleton in such terms. However, the structural components of our tissues are not like that at all. They all perform many functions and contribute in various ways to the phenomenon that we call life. They are being continuously broken down and replaced by new tissue components.

Proteins are thus essential components of our food but unfortunately also the most expensive. Inadequate protein in the diet can lead to insufficient development of the body and even to serious illness. Kwashiorkor is one example of undernourishment that exists among the poorer nations of the world.

It may be that in the discussion above we have given the impression that nitrogen is unnecessary for the production of energy. This is strictly speaking not so, but the amount of protein used for this purpose is limited in comparison with the other components of food, namely fats and carbohydrates.

The nitrogen present in the air is not used by body tissues and is not generally taken up by them in any significant amounts. Various lower forms of life, like nitrogen fixing bacteria, make more efficient use of it.

CHAPTER 3

Minerals and Electrolytes

Apart from the four elements discussed in the previous chapter, there are others that are absolutely essential for life, despite the fact that they are found only in relatively low concentrations in animal and plant tissues.

The name *mineral* brings to mind something which is obtained through the mining process, viz, ores and precious stones, and certainly not the constituents of the human body. Although we know today that the latter contains significant amounts of numerous elements, the name mineral has been retained for historical reasons, since most of the elements concerned were first obtained from underground deposits, and by analogy a number of them are "deposited" in bone, from whence they can be recovered by the body when needed.

In tissue fluids most minerals are present either in the ionic form or as part of compounds. Ions are, as has been noted in the previous chapter, subunits that carry an electrical charge. When ions are present in aqueous solution as is the case in the tissue fluids, they are capable of conducting electricity and are therefore frequently referred to as *electrolytes*.

Sodium (Symbol Na)

Sodium is present in the highest concentrations in the fluid circulating between cells of tissues; the so-called *extracellular* fluid, the composition of which is very similar to sea water. The intracellular fluid on the other hand is relatively poor in sodium. The reasons for the concentration difference between the two fluid compartments is two-fold. Firstly the cell wall does not permit considerable amounts of sodium ions to pass through it. Secondly, the minute quantities of sodium that do manage to get through the cell wall are taken out of the cell immediately by an *active transport* process referred to as the *sodium pump*. The transport of sodium across cell membranes is very closely related to the creation of an *electrical potential difference* across the membranes of cells.[1] This in turn is important in the

---

[1] This phenomenon has been described in the companion to this volume, *Elementary Medical Biophysics*, by G. G. Járos and B. J. Meyer.

transmission of nerve *impulses*, in muscle *contraction* and in *secretion* by glands, and other similar physiological phenomena without which life is impossible. Apart from these, sodium is of the greatest importance in the regulation of the *hydrogen ion concentration* and in the regulation of the *water balance* in the body (see chapters 5 and 11).

The amount of sodium in the body must be kept constant at all times to ensure normal physiological functioning of various tissues, i.e., the amount of sodium ingested must therefore equal sodium lost from the body. However we only require very small amounts of this element since only very small amounts of sodium are lost from the body and our food usually contains the required amounts. Why is it then that we sometimes feel compelled to add it to our food and that animals and sometimes also humans show a "hunger" for salt? There is no simple answer to these questions. Humans have used salt since the very earliest times as a preserving agent and as a condiment, and much of our desire for it is an acquired taste.

Losses of sodium occur through sweating, via the urine and in the faeces, the first two avenues being the most important. Sweating takes place only intermittently in a hot environment, or consequent to strenuous physical exercise. Travellers in desert areas must consume additional amounts of salt to compensate for losses incurred during sweating.

The formation of urine proceeds almost continuously. The main purpose of this is to rid the body of its waste products as well as of substances that are present in excess in order to regulate their concentration. The formation of urine will be discussed in detail in chapter 5. Suffice it to say at this stage that the excretion of sodium is achieved by the processes of *filtration* and *active reabsorption*. Sodium actually leaves the bloodstream in one particular region of the kidneys, and some is reabsorbed later according to the needs of the body. What is not reabsorbed is excreted. Hence by regulating the reabsorption, the excretion is regulated indirectly. The hormone *aldosterone* exercises a regulating function by stimulating the active reabsorption of sodium. In cases of sodium deficiency in the body aldosterone limits the loss in the kidneys. Some other hormones have similar but less pronounced effects to aldosterone. These are *deoxycorticosterone*, *cortisol*, the *oestrogens* and *progesterone*. All these hormones will be discussed again in chapter 12. It should be noted however that the excretion of sodium is very closely related to the excretion of water (see chapter 5) and hence the regulating effect of another hormone, the *antidiuretic hormone* (ADH), on sodium ion concentration. ADH increases the reabsorption of water in the kidneys and thereby dilutes the blood, and thus decreasing the sodium concentration.

Under certain abnormal circumstances the loss of salt from the body increases out of all proportion. This happens with serious diarrhoea or continuous vomiting. If we bear in mind what the functions of sodium are in the body we will be able to appreciate why certain nerve and muscle disturbances can be expected in the event of dramatic sodium loss. These include weakness, dizziness, loss of memory and fainting. Other attendant symptoms are often caused by the simultaneous loss of body water, this loss including reduction of intracellular water as well as extracellular water. The amount of circulating blood can decrease, bringing about serious changes in blood flow through the body. Severe thirst is experienced at the same time. The treatment of such cases includes among other things the administration of salt via the food or in the form of an intravenous saline drip.

In the extracellular fluid the ion which very frequently combines with sodium is chloride. In its crystalline form, the compound is our well known table salt.

Potassium (Symbol K)

By comparison with sodium, potassium is mainly found inside the cells of the body and is therefore said to be an *intracellular ion*. This is largely due to an active transport system coupled to, but working in the opposite direction, to the sodium pump. The two elements, viz, sodium and potassium, have in many respects opposite functions but in many instances their functions are complementary to one another. The creation of *electrical potential differences* across cell membranes is related to the exchange of sodium and potassium between intracellular and extracellular compartments. They both play a role in the regulation of the *hydrogen ion concentration* and the *water balance*, as well as in the *transport of carbon dioxide* by the red blood cells. We have mentioned earlier that chemical reactions are usually regulated by enzymes, about which more will be said in chapter 8. Some enzymes require what we call *co-factors* for efficient action. Potassium can act as co-factor for various enzymes, amongst others those that take part in the production of energy in the cells.

As potassium is mainly found intracellularly, the main sources of it are foods of animal and plant origin, the best being fruit juice, bananas and meat, and vegetable broths. Because potassium is so important for the body it is conserved by it. In this case, the hormone *aldosterone*, as well as the other hormones mentioned earlier in connection with sodium, control the excretion of potassium by the kidneys, but whereas the former is conserved by the body as a result of these hormones, the latter is excreted in increasing amounts. In cases of diarrhoea and vomiting, as well as in certain kidney disturbances, excessive loss of potassium can occur and result in disturbances of nerve and muscle function. Dizziness, loss of memory and muscle weakness are the usual signs. The heart muscle is especially sensitive to potassium levels that are lower than normal. In a case of coronary thrombosis, the heart muscle becomes excessively sensitive to this, and an increased potassium intake in the diet is necessary. Just as is the case with sodium, excessive loss of potassium causes pronounced thirst, indicating, concomitant disturbances of the water balance.

Calcium (Symbol Ca)

Most of the calcium in the body is found in the *skeleton*, which can then be considered as a place for storage of this ion. The compounds in which calcium is present in the skeleton lend strength to the bones and ensure the correct form of the body as well as the efficient action of muscles and joints during locomotion. When calcium is required by the tissues of the body it is released from its storage sites in the skeleton.

In tissue fluid, calcium is present in the ionic form and in the blood, both in the ionic and in a bound form. We have mentioned proteins as being components of tissues. There are also proteins present in the blood, known as plasma proteins or colloid substances. The calcium present in a bound form is usually bound to these proteins which assist in its transport to the tissues. In the tissues calcium is also involved in the origin of *electrical activity* in *nerve* and *muscle*, although in an entirely different way from sodium and potassium. Calcium is mainly found extracellularly but a certain percentage is found in the membranes, where it ensures stability of these, particularly in nerve and muscle tissue. If for any reason calcium is deficient, the nerve and muscle membranes become unstable and excitable, and excessive contractions called tetanic contractions make their appearance. Such contractions are extremely rapid, involving individual muscle fibres and causing prolonged cramps of the entire muscle mass concerned.

Calcium has another effect in muscle tissue which at first glance seems to be contradictory to the effect just discussed. In the muscle calcium serves as a *co-factor* for enzymes concerned with the release of the energy that is needed for efficient *muscle contraction*. Reduced calcium levels mean weaker contractions that are especially evident in the case of the heart muscle. Thus while a shortage of calcium causes muscular cramps in skeletal muscle, it also causes the weakening of the heart muscle.

Calcium is also a co-factor for enzymes involved in other reactions, the most important of which are those taking part in the *clotting of blood*. The function of blood clotting is to prevent loss of blood in the case of injury to the blood vessels, and is therefore a normal re-action of the body. It is a very complex process involving many factors, one of which is ionic calcium. Without the presence of calcium, blood will not clot. However, sometimes it is important to prevent blood from clotting, as for example in the case of blood intended for transfusion purposes, and in the case of blood samples collected for diagnostic purposes. One of the ways in which blood clotting can be prevented is by removing the calcium ions from it. This can be achieved by adding substances that bind with calcium and in the process form insoluble compounds. Examples of substances that can be added are sodium or potassium oxalate, or sodium or potassium citrate. In this case a so-called exchange reaction takes place; sodium citrate plus calcium ions, giving us sodium ions plus calcium citrate, which is a poorly soluble product and which does not readily yield calcium ions in solution.

Calcium is present in all foods to a lesser or greater extent. The best sources are milk, cereals, fruits and vegetables, in which it can exist in the ionic or bound forms. In certain cases the bound calcium is not taken up by the body. Carnivorous animals obtain most of their calcium from bones, which are digested by the hydrochloric acid in the stomach juices. Cattle are fed with bone meal to supplement grazing which may be low in calcium.

Calcium is generally lost from the body via the urine and faeces. The calcium content of the body must be kept constant to ensure continued health. This implies a sensitive control mechanism such as is usually achieved by hormones. The regulation of calcium levels in the body involves the action of three hormones, viz, *parathormone*, *thyrocalcitonin*, and 1,25-DHC (1,25 *dihydroxycholecalciferol*). The latter is produced in the kidney from an activated component of our food, viz, vitamin D (see chapter 12). Precursors of this vitamin are present in oils and vegetable fats, as well as in cod liver oil. They are taken up in the alimentary canal and transported by the blood to the skin where the activation takes place by the ultraviolet rays of the sun. This activated vitamin D is then converted into the final hormone in the kidneys. 1,25-DHC is required for the absorption of calcium from the alimentary canal. When the vitamin D precursors are absent from the diet or when growing children or animals are not exposed to sufficient sunlight, the disease known as rickets develops. It is characterised by insufficient growth and development of the bones and teeth as well as various bone malformations.

Rickets is an example of the deficiency diseases caused by an insufficient vitamin or mineral intake. Other diseases of this nature will be mentioned later.

Parathormone stimulates the active reabsorption of calcium in the kidneys as well as the relase of calcium from the bone, thus having the effect of increasing the blood calcium concentration. Thyrocalcitonin on the other hand stimulates the deposition of calcium in the bones, thus reducing blood calcium (see also chapter 12).

Magnesium (Symbol Mg)

Magnesium is found in the blood, and in the tissues it occurs both intra- and extracellularly. Like calcium it is stored mainly in the bone. It is of importance in various physiological processes, the most important of which is the *transfer of impulses, from nerve to muscle*. These impulses originate in the brain, are transmitted along the nerve fibres, and are then transferred to the muscles. This is achieved by the production of a transmitter substance, for example acetylcholine, that is released by the nerve, and diffuses to the muscle, initiating muscle contraction. Magnesium plays a role in the production of the transmitter substances. It most probably acts as a co-factor for enzymes that are concerned with the metabolism of the transmitter. It is also a *co-factor*, like calcium, in other enzyme-controlled reactions, mainly those concerned with *energy production* in cells.

It is assumed that our magnesium requirements present no problems since there appears to be sufficient present in our food. The body has special mechanisms whereby its magnesium levels are kept constant. In case of disturbances of these mechanisms, muscle and nerve function become disturbed. Muscular weakness and mental depression are prominent signs. In cattle increased excitability and tetanic contractions can be observed in magnesium deficiency states.

Iron (Symbol Fe)

Iron is involved in *energy production* in all forms of life. As mentioned in the previous chapter, oxygen is necessary for the combustion which takes place in the mitochondria in the tissue cells. Iron assists in the transport of oxygen both from the lungs to the cells as well as inside the cells to the final sites of energy production. In this capacity iron is present in the *haemoglobin* of the red blood cells, the *myoglobin* in muscle cells and the *cytochromes* and *cytochrome oxidase* within the cells. (The latter are concerned with energy production. Cytochrome oxidase is an enzyme, see chapters 8 and 10).

Iron is actually a poisonous substance, and like many heavy elements it is capable of forming insoluble compounds with tissue enzymes, thereby inactivating them and damaging the tissue concerned. Despite this the body requires iron and therefore it is obvious that it must be handled very carefully. Only what is actually required must be absorbed by the body, and during its storage the formation of insoluble substances must be avoided. The absorption of iron from the alimentary canal is regulated by *vitamin C* (ascorbic acid) on the one hand and by a special protein in the blood on the other. This carrier protein, called *transferrin* binds with the absorbed iron and renders it harmless for the body. The iron is then taken to the liver or spleen where it is bound again with a protein to form *ferritin*, the form in which it is stored, or to the red bone marrow for red blood cell production.

Iron, once taken up by the body, is not lost easily. Very little is excreted normally, and this excretion occurs through the bile and by exfoliation of dead skin cells. The cells within the body are replaced continuously and the iron released from them is re-used. Red blood cells which contain large amounts of iron in their haemoglobin only live for about 120 days, after which they are broken down in special cells belonging to the *Reticuloendothelial system* (RE-system). The iron that is freed is transported back to the red bone marrow for further production of haemoglobin or to the liver or spleen for storage.

Among our foods liver is the best source of iron, followed by meat, fruit and vegetables. When iron is deficient, *anaemia* can develop. This is characterised by a deficiency of haemoglobin and can be caused by other factors as well, apart from an iron deficiency. The affected individual appears pale, is short of breath and complains of weakness and fatigue. The deficiency can be caused by inadequate amounts of iron in the diet, by inefficient absorption due to intestinal disturbances, or due to vitamin C deficiency or by severe loss of blood. The latter can occur suddenly or slowly as is often the case in patients with cancer of the alimentary canal.

In women small amounts of iron are regularly lost during menstruation. During pregnancy considerable amounts of iron are transferred to the developing foetus. This is necessary for the production of haemoglobin and other iron-containing compounds in the foetus as well as for storage during the period of suckling, since milk is deficient in iron. The iron requirements of the female are therefore greater and more variable than those of the male, a fact which merits more attention than is usually paid to it.

Excessive amounts of iron can sometimes be absorbed by the body. This occurs in South Africa amongst the African population for reasons which are still unclear. It is thought that their use of iron pots for the preparation of their food may be one factor involved. Another possible way of increasing body iron to dangerous levels is through the injection and intravenous transfusion of iron-containing preparations. The excess is usually deposited in the form of an insoluble compound called *haemosiderin*. The disease is called *haemosiderosis* or *cytosiderosis* and manifests itself in serious malfunction of organs like the liver, pancreas, kidneys and others.

Chlorine (Symbol Cl)

The most abundant anion in the tissues of the body is the *chloride* ion, and is usually found in association with sodium ions, with which it forms sodium chloride, generally known as table salt. In the stomach chloride ions associate with hydrogen ions to form *hydrochloric acid*, an important compound in the digestion of foods. More will be said of it in chapters 5 and 9. Another function of chloride ions is in connection with the *transport of carbon dioxide* in the blood (see chapter 11) and the ion also serves as a *co-factor* for a number of enzymes.

Phosphorus (Symbol P)

Phosphorus is not found in its elemental form in the body, but always in combination with oxygen. The two together with hydrogen form a negative charged group of subunits or negative radical usually referred to as the *orthophosphate* ion, since in solutions it behaves as an ion. The orthophosphate ion can bind with the cations, potassium, sodium, calcium and magnesium as well as with large molecules containing carbon. Apart from a few proteins the best known of the large molecular compounds containing a phosphate radical is *adenosine triphosphate* or ATP, which is the most important storage form of energy in the body. This compound will be discussed in detail together with other high energy substances, in chapters 7 and 10. The orthophosphate ion is often referred to by the symbol Pi in biochemical writings and is more generally simply known as the *phosphate* ion. In general when carbon-containing substances bind with the phosphate ion, their energy increases and they are said to be *activated* (see chapter 10). In conjunction with sodium and potassium, phosphate ions play an important role in the regulation of the *hydrogen ion concentration* of the body (see chapter 11). The largest concentration of phosphate exists in combination with calcium in *bone*. The regulation of phosphate levels is therefore closely related to that of calcium and is mainly a function of the hormones, *parathormone* and 1,25 *DHC* (see chapter 12).

If the diet is a balanced one, the intake of phosphates should be adequate. There are many regions in the world where the phosphate content of the soil is low, and deficiencies of this element arise in both plants and animals. Humans dependant on these food sources will similarly become deficient in phosphorus. Such cases are characterised by poor growth and weak development of bones and teeth.

Sulphur (Symbol S)

Sulphur exists in a great variety of compounds in the body, mainly in conjunction with proteins. It forms part of superficial body structures such as skin, hair, nails, horns and so on.

The trace elements

This group consists of elements which are only present in the body in very minute quantities but which are nevertheless essential for life. While the concentrations of the previously mentioned elements are usually expressed in grams or milligrams[2] per 100 millilitres of tissue fluid, those of the trace elements are usually expressed in *micrograms* or sometimes even in *nanograms*. The group consists of *copper, manganese, cobalt, zinc, molybdenum, selenium, fluorine* and *iodine*. Apart from iodine, these elements form either part of *enzymes* or of *co-factors* necessary for certain enzymes. The manner in which these elements are handled apparently differs in humans and animals, and is still in many ways obscure. It should be remembered that in concentrations exceeding the normal these elements are poisonous and thus potentially harmful for the body.

Copper (Cu) is carried in blood plasma in a similar way to iron by a special protein, called *caeruloplasmin*. A certain amount is also found in the *red blood cells*, again bound to a protein. Copper is needed for the normal development and functioning of *nerve* and *bone* tissue, and for the production of *haemoglobin* in developing red blood cells. It forms an important part of the enzyme, *cytochrome oxidase* and is thus of special importance in oxidation processes (see chapter 10).

Manganese (Mn) is carried in blood plasma by the special protein *transmanganin*. It is an important co-factor for some enzymes concerned with metabolism.

Cobalt (Co) is found in *vitamin B$_{12}$* (also known as *cyanocobalamine*), which in turn is a co-factor for several enzymes. It is especially important for the normal growth and development of *red blood cells*.

Vitamin B$_{12}$ is absorbed from the alimentary canal with the assistance of a so-called *intrinsic factor* secreted by the stomach. Deficiency of the vitamin or insufficient absorption thereof can lead to an inadequate maturation of red blood cells, resulting in pernicious anaemia (perniciosus = destructive, Latin). (See chapter 12 for further detail.)

---

[2] milligram (mg) = 0,001g (or 10^{-3}g); microgram (μg) = 0,000001g (or 10^{-6}g); nanogram (ng) = 0,000000001g (or 10^{-9}g).

Zinc (*Zn*) forms part of the *enzyme carbonic anhydrase* which is concerned in the utilization and transport of carbon dioxide in the body (see chapter 11).

Molybdenum (*Mo*) is a *co-factor* for enzymes.

Selenium (*Se*) is associated with *vitamin E*, or *tocopherol*, in preventing oxidation of certain membrane constituents, acting thus as an anti-oxidant.

Fluorine, chlorine, bromine and *iodine* are elements generally referred to as *halogens* (halos = table salt, Greek) since they were first obtained from sea salt. They occur in the body in the form of anions.

Fluorine (*F*) is necessary for the development and maintenance of *teeth*, and a deficiency of this element leads to tooth decay. In high concentrations it is extremely toxic. Small amounts are present in water and the vegetation. In certain cities throughout the world fluorine is added to the drinking water to prevent dental caries in children, but because of the inherent *dangers* this practice is under very strict control.

Iodine (*I*) exists either in the elemental form or in the form of compounds, the commonest being the group known as *iodides*. It is present in the body in the ionic (iodide) form or in a protein-bound form, and forms part of the *thyroid hormone, thyroxin*. This hormone is very important in regulating the energy producing reactions of the body (see chapters 10 and 12). Iodides are present in drinking water, sea water, fish, vegetables and meat, and are generally added to table salt.

An iodine deficiency leads to the appearance of a goitre, or markedly enlarged thyroid gland that is ineffectually attempting to produce sufficient amounts of thyroid hormone. Deficiencies are limited to certain regions of the world and the appearance of goitre can be prevented by supplementing the diet with iodised salt.

The well-known tincture of iodine is an alcoholic solution of the element which is used as a *disinfectant* in cases of skin injury.

Other elements found in tissues

The presence of a great number of the 103 known elements can be demonstrated in tissues using sensitive analytical methods. Some of these elements exist in surprisingly constant amounts in the body, which may indicate that they have some *biological function*. Examples of these are *nickel* (Ni), *chromium* (Cr), *cadmium* (Cd), *vanadium* (V), *silicon* (Si), *boron* (B) and *bromine* (Br). A few elements that may enter the body accidentally through the respiratory system or the alimentary tract, can be *dangerous* and cause serious harm if their concentration in the body reaches certain proportions. Examples of these are *lead* (Pb), *mercury* (Hg), *arsenic* (As) and *strontium* (Sr).

A few of the other elements are used for various *therapeutic* and *diagnostic purposes*, for instance *technecium* (Tc), *indium* (In) and *barium* (Ba).

A full list of elements appears in Appendix A.

CHAPTER 4

Symbols, Reactions and Equations

Up to this point we have introduced all the biologically important
elements and have taken note of the symbols used to designate them
in chemical or biochemical work. In the preceding chapter when we
were considering the way blood can be prevented from coagulating
we made acquaintance with a *reaction*, which was expressed as:

Sodium citrate + calcium ions = calcium citrate + sodium ions.

What is written down here is in fact a *chemical equation*. In the first
instance this expression is a description of a chemical reaction. It
tells us that the compound sodium citrate reacts with calcium ions to
form the compound calcium citrate and sodium ions. In addition to
this, the equation provides important information in connection with
the relative amounts of the different substances that are involved in
the reaction. The equality sign between the two sides of the equation
means that the amount of substances on the left hand side equals
that on the right hand side. Although no numbers appear in the
above equation the implication is clear that *one part* of sodium citrate
reacts with *one part* of calcium ions to give *one part* of calcium citrate
and *one part* of sodium ions. However, as it stands, the equation does
not provide information about the structure of the substances participating in the reaction.

We know that all substances are built up of subunits of matter,
viz, atoms, ions and molecules with which we have already become
acquainted. However, the above equation does not tell us in what
proportion the subunits are combined with one another. If all this
additional information were to be verbally included in the above
expression it would certainly become very complicated indeed. One
can, however, avoid these complications by using symbols and numbers which will provide all the necessary information, instead of the
verbally descriptive expression; in other words we can develop a
more manageable type of chemical shorthand.

The formation of ions

As has been seen earlier, ions carry an electric charge, which is negative in the case of anions and positive in the case of cations. The process of ion formation, whereby the atom gains or loses one or more

electrons, is called *ionization*. It is also a well known fact that like electrical charges repel and unlike charges attract one another. By using these facts it is possible to explain how reactions take place between the various subunits concerned. We can begin by considering ions as the active subunits of elements.

As we have seen in chapter 1 atoms and ions are composed of three kinds of particles, viz, protons, neutrons and electrons (Fig. 4.1). The protons and neutrons are found in the nucleus and the electrons in orbits around it. The number of protons possessed by a certain element is called the atomic number. We can compare the atom with our solar system in which the planets orbit around the sun. However, the analogy ends here. In the solar system, each planet has its own particular orbit, but this is not the case with the electrons of atoms. The different orbits can contain *one or more* electrons according to the element or electron orbit in question. *There is, however, a limit to the number of electrons a certain orbit can accommodate.* In the orbit closest to the nucleus, the so-called *K-orbit,* there can be a maximum of *two* electrons. If further electron orbits are present in a particular atom, and these are designated in order the *L-, M-* and *N-orbits,* the maximum number of electrons which these orbits can hold are *eight, eighteen* and *thirty-two,* respectively. However, should the L-, M- or N-orbit be the outer one they can each only accommodate eight electrons. Thus the maximum number of electrons that can be held in an outermost orbit is eight.

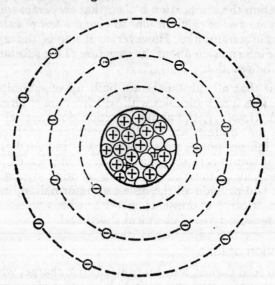

FIG. 4.1   Schematic representation of the structure of an atom; $\oplus$ = proton, O = neutron, $\ominus$ = electron.

One of the most important concepts in the structural organisation of subunits in the formation of atoms is that of *stability*: the most stable form being that in which the outermost *electron orbit* is *either completely filled or is completely empty*. It has been mentioned that in an atom the number of protons equals the number of electrons and the atom is therefore electrically neutral. In only a few instances is the outer orbit completely filled with electrons. The elements in which this occurs are very stable indeed. Helium (He) is for example an element with two protons and therefore two electrons. Both of these are in the K-orbit,[1] which in this case is the outermost orbit and is thus full and the atom is stable. Other elements that are very stable are neon (Ne), argon (Ar), krypton (Kr), xenon (Xe) and radon (Ra).

Valency

The ability of elements to combine with each other is called the *valency* of the element (Latin, valens = strong), which depends upon the number of electrons present or the lack of electrons in the outer orbits. These electrons are accordingly referred to as *valency electrons*. Generally the valency is numerically equal to the charge carried by the ions. For example hydrogen (H^+), sodium (Na^+) and chlorine (Cl^-) are *monovalent* atoms or ions, calcium (Ca^{++}) and magnesium (Mg^{++}) are *divalent* and iron (Fe^{+++}) is *trivalent*.

However, not all elements can form ions readily in which cases the valency has to be inferred in a different way. Nitrogen (N), for example has seven protons, with two electrons in the K-orbit and five in the L-orbit. For stability, three electrons need to be taken up to fill the outer orbit. Nitrogen is therefore a *trivalent* atom. Oxygen, on the other hand has six electrons in its outer orbit, needing two for stability. It is therefore a *divalent* atom. On the same basis carbon is tetravalent (Greek, tetartos = fourth).

Different elements can behave similarly if their valency orbits have the same composition. We find therefore that elements such as sodium with one valency electron, aluminium (Al) with three, phosphorus (P) with five and chlorine with seven behave completely differently chemically and physiologically. On the other hand sodium, potassium and lithium (Li) all have one valency electron and behave similarly despite the differences in gross composition of their atoms.

---

[1] Hydrogen and Helium are the only two elements possessing the K-orbit as the only, and at the same time, the outermost orbit. These elements are exceptional in that here the K-orbit can only hold a maximum of two electrons and not the eight possible for an outer orbit as mentioned earlier.

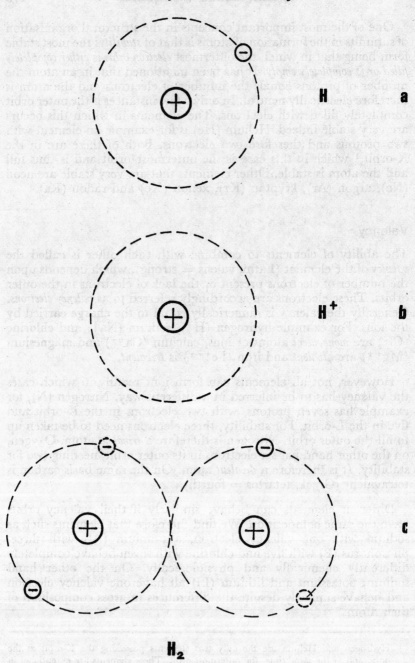

FIG. 4.2 The three subunits of hydrogen: (a) atom, (b) ion, and (c) molecule.

A number of elements can exist in more than one valency state, for instance sulphur can have a valency of four or six, copper one or two (Cu^+ or Cu^{++}), iron two or three (Fe^{++} or Fe^{+++}) and so on. The reasons for this are beyond the scope of this text and need not concern us at the moment. The most important of these particular elements for biological systems is iron, and it is functional in either of its valency states.

The formation of molecules — Covalent bonds

Another way in which stability can be reached is by avoiding unfilled orbits through the *sharing of electrons* between two or more atoms (Fig. 4.2). When two hydrogen atoms (H) come close enough, the single electron in the K-orbit of one of them can move across the K-orbit of the other making it momentarily full. The other can do the same and the two electrons therefore oscillate between the two orbits. At any given time the two subunits have opposite charges and exercise a force of attraction on each other, which tends to keep them together. This combination is called a *molecule*. The hydrogen molecule consists of two atoms and is consequently indicated by the symbol H_2, the subscript signifying the number of atoms present. The force of attraction between the two atoms is known as a *chemical bond*. Chlorine atoms can behave in the same way, when they combine to form a chlorine molecule (Cl_2), each of them donating one of the seven M-orbit electrons to the electron pair that they then share (Fig. 4.3a). The outer (M-) orbit of each atom is thus momentarily filled, conferring stability on the combination.

The abovementioned bond, in which an electron pair is shared between two atoms is termed a *covalent bond*. When the two atoms are of the same element they always bind covalently. When the two atoms are different other possibilities for binding are presented as well as the more common covalent bonds.

Nitrogen (N) is a trivalent atom and for stability, three electrons need to be taken up to fill the outer orbit. These can be donated, for instance, by three hydrogen atoms, forming the ammonia molecule (Fig. 4.3b). From this figure it should be clear that there are three electron pairs that are shared, the one nitrogen atom providing three, one to each pair, and the three hydrogen atoms one each. For this reason the compound ammonia can be represented as NH_3.

Water molecules (Fig. 4.3c) consist of one oxygen atom bound to two hydrogen atoms or H_2O. Oxygen is a divalent atom, needing two electrons for stability, which it can also obtain from two hydrogen atoms. The student should at this stage look at the compounds represented in Fig. 4.3a, b and c. It will be seen that in each atom represented the requirement for stability, viz, a completely full outer orbit, has been satisfied.

Multiple covalent bonds

Carbon (C) atoms can also combine with one another by sharing electrons. Carbon (atomic number 6) has a valency of four, thus lacking four electrons for stability. Two carbon atoms can combine to share an electron pair (Fig. 4.3d) thus forming a covalent bond and reducing the electron deficit in each of the carbon atoms to three. These can be provided for instance by six hydrogen atoms to form the compound C_2H_6 (Fig. 4.3e). The two carbon atoms can also share two electron pairs (Fig. 4.3f), this being done through a *double covalent bond* or simply a *double bond*. The electrons still lacking, two in each carbon atom, can again be provided by four hydrogen atoms to form the compound C_2H_4 (Fig. 4.3g). Two carbon atoms can also share three electron pairs forming a triple covalent bond or simply a *triple bond* to form the compound C_2H_2 (Fig. 4.3i). The same can happen in the case of two nitrogen atoms (Fig. 4.3h).

Ionic bonds

It has been mentioned earlier that ions have a stable structure but at the same time they are electrically charged. *Oppositely charged ions attract each other* and, when they approach near enough to one another they bind with one another by means of the opposite electrical charges without disturbance in their stability. This type of bond is called an *electrovalent* or *ionic bond*, and in it the forces of attraction are much weaker than in covalent bonds and an ionic bond is thus often referred to as an *association* rather than a bond. Sodium ions (Na^+) and chloride ions (Cl^-) can, for instance, combine or rather *associate* to form *sodium chloride* (NaCl) which we all know as our familiar *table salt*. If solid, table salt occurs in the form of this association, but as soon as salt is dissolved in water some of the sodium chloride molecules break up or *dissociate* to form sodium and chloride ions again. Since the ions in such a solution are charged, the solution can conduct electricity and is consequently referred to as an *electrolyte* solution.

The association and dissociation of sodium chloride can be represented by the following equation:

$$Na^+ + Cl^- \rightleftharpoons NaCl$$

This equation not only tells us that one sodium ion combines with one chloride ion to form one molecule of sodium chloride, but also, the presence of the double arrows, indicates that the reaction is *reversible* and represents both the processes of association and dissociation. Both are possible depending on the concentrations of the participating substances. This particular aspect will be discussed in more detail in chapter 5.

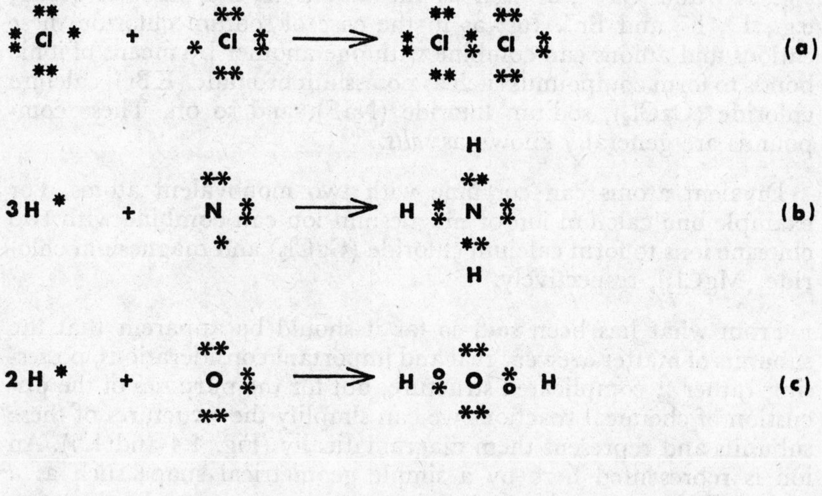

FIG. 4.3 The formation of molecules and bonds (only the electrons in the outer orbit are shown). (a) chlorine molecule (Cl_2), ammonia molecule (NH_3), (c) water molecule (H_2O), covalent bond between two carbon atoms, (e) ethane molecule, (f) double covalent bond between two carbon atoms, (g) ethylene molecule (C_2H_4), (h) nitrogen molecule (N_2), and (i) acetylene molecule (C_2H_2).

In the foregoing chapters mention was made of *metallic cations*, e.g., K^+ and Ca^{++}, as well as the anions in the halogen group, e.g., I^-, F^- and Br^-. Just as in the case of sodium chloride these cations and anions can combine with one another by means of ionic bonds to form compounds such as potassium bromide (KBr), calcium chloride ($CaCl_2$), sodium fluoride (NaF), and so on. These compounds are generally known as *salts*.

Divalent atoms can combine with two monovalent atoms. For example one calcium ion or magnesium ion can combine with two chlorine ions to form calcium chloride ($CaCl_2$) and magnesium chloride ($MgCl_2$), respectively.

From what has been said so far it should be apparent that the subunits of matter are very real and important considerations, possessing rather a complicated structure, but for the purposes of the discussion of chemical reactions we can simplify the structures of these subunits and represent them diagramatically (Fig. 4.4 and 4.5). An ion is represented here by a simple geometrical shape such as a square. In the case of an anion the extra electrons can be shown as protrusions (Fig. 4.4a, b, c), and in the case of cations the lack of electrons, by corresponding recesses (Fig. 4.4d, e, f). By using these diagrams one can visualize how the various opposite charged ions can attract and combine with one another to form electrically neutral compounds (Fig. 4.5).

Co-ordinate Covalent Bonds (Dative bonds)

Because of the instability of ionic bonds and the continuous dissociations and associations of the ions concerned, compounds containing such bonds are of very great importance in living systems and we shall encounter them frequently in the pages which follow. Apart from ionic and covalent bonds there is a third type of bond that we should take note of, the so-called *co-ordinate covalent* or *dative bond*. This is similar to a normal covalent bond in that there is again a sharing of an electron pair. However, while in a covalent bond each of the atoms donates equal numbers of electrons to the electron pair or pairs, in a dative bond all the pairs of electrons concerned are donated by one of the atoms only. The adjective, *dative*, takes its origin from the Latin, *dato*, I give up or yield and is therefore in a sense descriptive. The pairs of the electrons concerned are often referred to as *lone pairs*. Such a pair may be seen in the structure of ammonia (Fig. 4.6a) while the dative bond may be seen in the structure of the ammonium ion and ammonium chloride (Fig. 4.6b and c respectively) as well as in that of the biologically important orthophosphoric acid.

Formulae

We have used symbols and subscript numbers to indicate molecules of a large number of elements and compounds such as H_2, Cl_2, NH_3, H_2O, C_2H_4, C_2H_6, KBr, etc. These combinations of symbols and subscripts are known as *formulae*. A formula is not only a useful form of chemical shorthand, but also indicates the relative proportions of the different atoms represented in a compound. The diagrams of the compounds represented in Fig. 4.3 are termed electronic structure formulas, which apart from indicating what atoms are present in the molecule, tell us also of the type of bonds present in the compound concerned.

Radicals

In the previous chapter we encountered a group of compounds, such as sulphates, phosphates, citrates and oxalates. These names actually represent negatively charged groups of closely bound atoms called *acidic radicals* as they are mainly derived from the dissociation of acids. For example:

$$H_2SO_4 \rightleftharpoons 2H^+ + SO_4^=$$

H_2SO_4 is a sulphuric acid molecule, and

$SO_4^=$ is a sulphate radical

or

$$H_3PO_4 \rightleftharpoons 3H^+ + PO_4^{\equiv}$$

H_3PO_4 is a phosphoric acid molecule

PO_4- is a phosphate radical.

These acids and radicals will be discussed again in detail in chapter 5, but the most important of them are presented for consideration at this stage in Table 4.1.

Table 4.1   Acids and acid radicals

ACID		RADICAL	
Name of Acid	*Symbol*	*Name of radical or ion*	*Symbol*
Carbonic acid	H_2CO_3	carbonate (divalent)	$CO_3^=$
		bicarbonate (monovalent)	$HCO_3^=$
Nitric acid	HNO_3	nitrate	$NO_3^=$
Nitrous acid	HNO_2	nitrite	$NO_2^=$
Orthophosphoric acid	H_3PO_4	phosphate (trivalent)	$PO_4^{\equiv}$
		acid phosphate (divalent)	$HPO_4^=$
		basic phosphate (monovalent)	$H_2PO_4^-$
Sulphuric acid	H_2SO_4	sulphate (divalent)	$SO_4^=$
Hydrogen sulphide	H_2S	sulphide (divalent)	$S^=$

In chemical reactions radicals behave like anions and the two names are therefore often used indiscriminately.

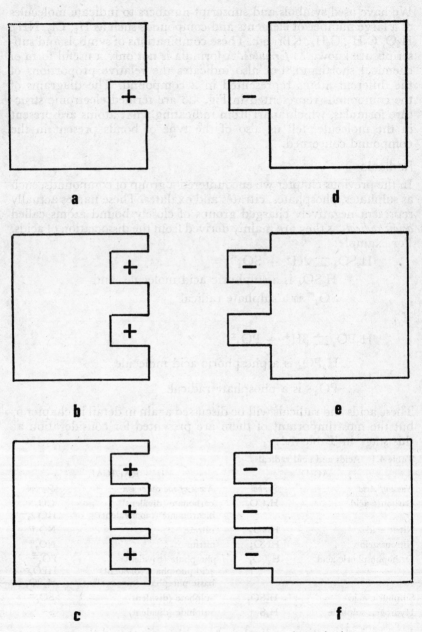

FIG. 4.4 Schematic representation of positive and negative ions.

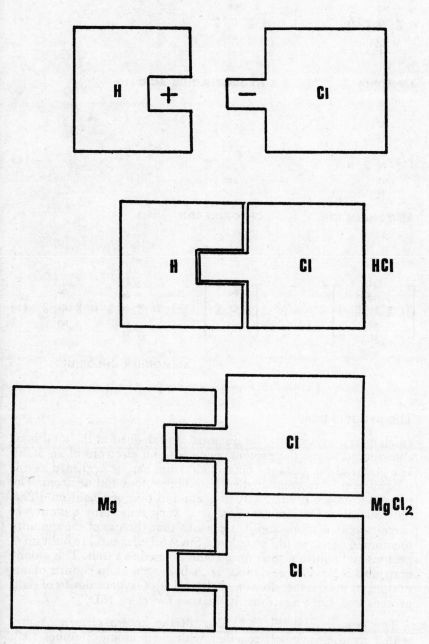

FIG. 4.5   The formation of hydrochloric acid and magnesium chloride.

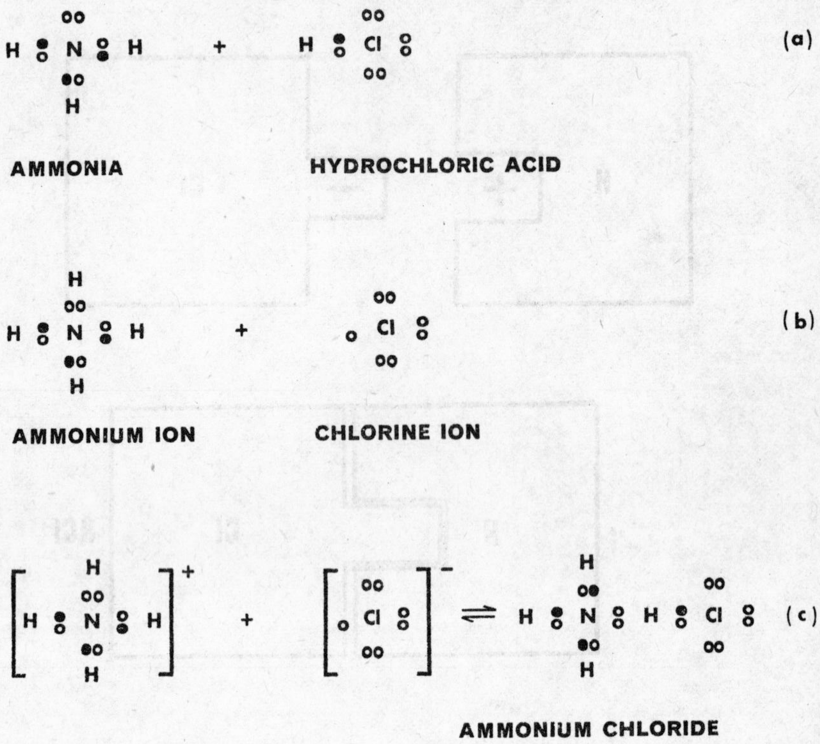

FIG. 4.6   The formation of ammonium chloride.

The periodic table

In chapter 1 *atomic mass* was discussed and defined as the total mass contributed by all the protons, neutrons and electrons of an atom. For practical purposes the mass of electrons can be neglected as it is insignificant when compared with that of protons and neutrons. The mass of a proton is $1,657 \times 10^{-24}$ gram and that of a neutron differs only slightly. The atomic mass is a very important quantity in chemical calculations and it is obvious that the use of the quantity mentioned above would be tedious. Since all elements are built up of protons and neutrons their mass could be used as a unit. This atomic mass unit is termed the dalton, D. A hydrogen atom consists of one proton; its mass is therefore one dalton (1D). Oxygen consists of eight protons and eight neutrons; its mass is therefore 16D.

The *periodic table* (Fig. 4.7) lists all the known elements represented by their symbols together with their atomic number (left, below the symbol), and the atomic mass (above the symbol at the right). The table extends from the lightest element, viz, hydrogen,

PERIODIC TABLE OF THE ELEMENTS

1 H 1																		4 He 2
7 Li 3	9 Be 4											11 B 5	12 C 6	14 N 7	16 O 8	19 F 9	20 Ne 10	
23 Na 11	24 Mg 12											27 Al 13	28 Si 14	31 P 15	32 S 16	35 Cl 17	40 Ar 18	
39 K 19	40 Ca 20	45 Sc 21	48 Ti 22	51 V 23	52 Cr 24	55 Mn 25	56 Fe 26	59 Co 27	59 Ni 28	64 Cu 29	65 Zn 30	70 Ga 31	73 Ge 32	75 As 33	79 Se 34	80 Br 35	84 Kr 36	
85 Rb 37	88 Sr 38	89 Y 39	91 Zr 40	93 Nb 41	96 Mo 42	98 Tc 43	101 Ru 44	103 Rh 45	106 Pd 46	108 Ag 47	112 Cd 48	115 In 49	119 Sn 50	122 Sb 51	128 Te 52	127 I 53	131 Xe 54	
133 Cs 55	137 Ba 56	139 La 57 *	178 Hf 72	181 Ta 73	184 W 74	186 Re 75	190 Os 76	192 Ir 77	195 Pt 78	197 Au 79	201 Hg 80	204 Tl 81	207 Pb 82	209 Bi 83	210 Po 84	210 At 85	222 Rn 86	
223 Fr 87	226 Ra 88	227 Ac 89 **	104															

*	140 Ce 58	141 Pr 59	144 Nd 60	147 Pm 61	150 Sm 62	152 Eu 63	157 Gd 64	159 Tb 65	163 Dy 66	165 Ho 67	167 Er 68	169 Tm 69	173 Yb 70	175 Lu 71
**	232 Th 90	231 Pa 91	238 U 92	237 Np 93	242 Pu 94	243 Am 95	247 Cm 96	247 Bk 97	249 Cf 98	254 Es 99	253 Fm 100	256 Md 101	254 No 102	257 Lw 103

ATOMIC MASS → 65

SYMBOL → Zn

ATOMIC NUMBER → 30

through to the heaviest, viz, lawrencium. The symbols and values indicated in this table are used throughout the world in the portrayal of chemical formulas and chemical reaction, as well as for calculation purposes as we shall see shortly. The names of the elements shown in this table are listed in Appendix A.

The elements shown in the periodic table are not simply listed there but are placed there in horizontal periods according to the number of electron orbits present, and into vertical columns or groups according to the number of valency electrons present. Other considerations, which are beyond the scope of this text are also important in the grouping of the elements in this table. Period one elements have only the K-orbit, period 2 elements the K- and L-orbits and so on. In the first vertical column we find the elements which have only valency electron, viz, lithium, sodium, potassium, and so on and which behave in a similar way chemically. The second vertical column contains the divalent elements, amongst which are the biologically important calcium and magnesium. The elements in this column also have similar chemical and physiological properties. The halogens are to be found in vertical column 17. These monovalent elements require only one electron to fill their valency orbit. In the last column are to be found the so-called *inert* elements such as helium (He) and neon (Ne), and so on. All these have their outer orbits filled and all are very stable gases. When arranged in this fashion or ascending order the elements periodically exhibit similar chemical (and in some instances physiological) properties. Hence the name of the table.

By using the values given for atomic mass in the periodic table, the mass of molecules can easily be calculated by simply considering their formulas. The *molecular mass* of a hydrogen molecule (H_2) is therefore $2 \times 1 = 2D$. That of O_2 is $2 \times 16 = 32D$, of water, H_2O, $2 \times 1 + 16 = 18D$, of ethylene, $C_2H_6 = 2 \times 12 + 6 \times 1 = 30D$, and so on.

Introduction to chemical reactions

During the course of a chemical reaction chemical bonds are either formed or broken. If we ignite a mixture of hydrogen and oxygen (mixed in the correct proportions), a vigorous reaction takes place and water is formed. In this case the bonds holding together the oxygen atoms in the molecules (O_2) and hydrogen atoms in the molecules (H_2) are broken and new bonds arise with the formation of water molecules (H_2O). We can simply write these events as:

$$2H_2 + O_2 = 2H_2O$$

A chemical reaction leads therefore to a change in molecular structure. This usually is accompanied by the release or uptake of energy.

An important aspect of a chemical reaction is the *rate* at which it occurs. The rate can be influenced by various factors, such as temperature, concentration of reagents, enzymes, etc. These will be discussed in chapter 8.

If we return for the moment to the equation depicting the combination of hydrogen with oxygen to form water, a close examination will show that this equation is balanced, like all good equations should be. The same number of atoms entering the reaction also leave it, i.e., this number is the same on both sides of the equation, viz, four hydrogen and two oxygen atoms. This automatically means that the total mass of substances on both sides of the equation is equal.

Let us take another example. When sodium is dropped into water a vigorous reaction occurs and sodium hydroxide (NaOH) is formed, together with the evolution of hydrogen. We can write the equation as follows:

$$2Na + 2H_2O = 2NaOH + H_2$$

Putting the equation into words it reads:

Two sodium atoms combine with two water molecules to form two molecules of sodium hydroxide and one molecule of hydrogen.

It is often necessary to produce various compounds in the chemical laboratory. It is therefore useful to know the relative quantities of reactants that must be used in order to obtain the correct amount of the required compounds. We can easily calculate this with the aid of the equation describing the reaction and by using the atomic masses in the place of the symbols in the above equation (Na = 23D,H = 1D,O = 2D), thus:

$$(2 \times 23D) + 2(2D + 16D) = 2(23D + 16D + 1D) + (2 \times 1D)$$
$$\text{or} \quad 46D + 36D = 80D + 2D$$
$$\text{or} \quad 82D = 82D$$

Therefore, the atomic masses on both sides of the equation balance out. *Although in the above case the unit of atomic mass, the dalton has been used* any *unit of mass (e.g., gram, milligram, etc.) could have been employed,* e.g.:

$$46g\,Na + 36g\,H_2O = 80g\,NaOH + 2g\,H_2$$
$$\text{or} \quad 46mg\,Na + 36mg\,H_2O = 80mg\,NaOH + 2mg\,H_2$$

Whatever units we use, the proportions will always remain the same. This is fundamental to the use of chemical equations. Let us consider briefly two examples of how the above equation can be used.

Assume that we wish to make two lots of sodium hydroxide (NaOH) in 40 and 15 gram amounts respectively. To calculate the required amounts of reactants to produce 40g of NaOH is simple; since we need only use half the quantities of sodium and water indicated above, and to keep the correct proportions we simply halve all the terms in the equation thus:

$$23g\,Na + 18g\,H_2O = 40g\,NaOH + 1g\,H_2$$

In the second case the quantities have to be reduced in the proportion of 15/80 to produce the 15 gram of NaOH required, thus:

$$\text{the sodium to be used} \quad = \frac{15 \times 46}{80} = 8\,626 \text{ gram}$$

$$\text{and the water to be used} \quad = \frac{15 \times 36}{80} = 6\,750 \text{ gram}$$

CHAPTER 5

Water, Acids and Bases

The importance of water in the body

The most important compound in biological systems is undoubtedly water. We have only to think of people stranded in the desert without water, to appreciate its importance. In humans about 70% of the body mass consists of water. The extremely large number of chemical reactions in the body are made possible by the fact that the reacting subunits are dissolved in water. In solution many of the subunits assume an ionic form and also acquire greater mobility, making *chemical reactions* possible. Water also serves as a transport medium, both allowing molecular movement as in the case of *diffusion* as well as total movement as in the case of *circulation*. Water also helps with the stabilisation of body temperature as a result of its good *heat conducting ability*, and its *high specific heat*.

Water is also directly involved in many chemical reactions, one of the most important of them being *hydrolysis*. During this process large molecules are broken down to smaller ones by the participation of water in the reaction. The process of digestion in the digestive tract involves mainly hydrolysis of the various foodstuffs in the diet, to smaller products which are more readily absorbed (see chapter 9).

Distribution of water in the body

About two-thirds of body water is found in the cells (*intracellular fluid*) whilst the rest lies outside the cells (*extracellular fluid*). A part of this water constitutes the blood (*intravascular fluid*), some of it being within the red blood cells, the rest being present as the blood plasma. The blood serves as a transport medium for nutrients and for other substances needed by the cells, as well as for the waste products produced by the cells of various tissues.

Fluid mixtures

When two substances are evenly distributed within a container, one speaks of a mixture. If the substance present in the higher concentration happens to be a liquid, one speaks of a fluid mixture. The other substance present in the mixture can be in any of the physical states, viz, solid, liquid or gaseous. The living body is actually a fluid mixture, in most of its parts the basic fluid being water, although there are some areas, notably within the membranes of cells where the fluid is a fat-like substance.

A substance that is mixed with a liquid can behave in two ways. It may dissociate into smaller molecules and ions, or it can remain in the larger molecular form it had before mixing. The former type of mixture is called a *solution*, the liquid being the *solvent* and the other substance the *solute*. The molecules or ions of the solute distribute evenly in the spaces between the molecules of the solvent. When the available spaces are filled the solution is said to be saturated. We generally speak of substances which form a true solution (and this is one which is quite clear and transparent) as *crystalloids*. The name is an old one, merely indicating that many such substances can be prepared in a crystalline state.

The solubility of substances in different solvents is variable. For example electrolytes are generally soluble in water, but insoluble in fat-like substances, while oxygen and carbon dioxide are soluble in both. The solubility of substances in the same solvent can also vary. For example, carbon dioxide is about twenty times more soluble in fats than oxygen is. The solubility of these two gases is also dependent on the partial pressures which they exert in and above the mixture (see chapter 2).

If the substance that is mixed with a liquid is insoluble in that liquid, it may form a *suspension* or an *emulsion*. Such mixtures generally involve particles larger than those which pass into true solution in a liquid. In the case of large particles, these will mix with the particles of the solvent during vigorous shaking. Once this is stopped, however, the large particles sediment out rapidly. Since the particles are merely "suspended" between the particles of the solvent during the shaking, we call this type of mixture a suspension. In the case of somewhat smaller particles where sedimentation occurs at a relatively slow rate, we speak of a *colloidal solution* or *colloidal suspension*. Such solutions appear turbid, milky or opalescent. Milk is an example of a colloidal solution of milk proteins, while the plasma proteins are present in blood plasma in the same state. Particles which form this type of mixture are generally referred to as *colloids*.

When both components of the mixture are liquids, one speaks of an *emulsion*, which can be temporary or permanent according to the size of the droplets of the smaller constituent. Oil forms a temporary emulsion with water since after a while the oil droplets collect and form a layer on the top of the water. Milk is also an example of a temporary emulsion, since on standing, the large fat droplets rise to the surface in the form of cream. The skimmed milk remaining after removal of the cream is a colloidal solution of milk proteins, like casein, and other products. By the same token blood is also a complex mixture consisting of a solution of electrolytes, an emulsion of fats, a colloidal solution of plasma proteins and a suspension of cells.

Water gain and loss

Water present in our bodies is obtained from the foods that we eat and from the liquids that we drink. A certain amount of water is produced in the body during metabolic processes, this being referred to as *metabolic water*. The most important process by which metabolic water is formed is the oxidation of hydrogen during which energy is produced (see chapter 10). Some chemical reactions which involve dehydration release water during the breakdown of large molecules.

Since water is such an important constituent of tissues, it is essential that the amount present within the body tissues be regulated as finely as possible. Water is being continually lost from the body by various ways. One of these is in the form of water vapour present in the expired air. Since we are generally unaware of this, we speak of this as being an *insensible* loss of water. A second way is through the kidneys, where the waste products can only leave the body in the form of the aqueous solution which we call urine. A certain amount of water (500 - 2 000ml) per day must be used for this purpose. We speak of this as an *obligatory* water loss. Water is also lost from the surface of the skin during the process of sweating. Since the rate at which this occurs is variable and intimately concerned with the control of the body temperature, we refer to it as a *variable* water loss. When the amount of water lost through the urine or through sweat is excessive, it must be replenished. The diminution of body water gives rise to the sensation of thirst.

Water loss via the kidneys

Although the urine constitutes the most important avenue through which excess water can be eliminated, it must be borne in mind that it is also the most important route for the elimination of waste products formed in the tissues of the body and an important organ in the regulation of the composition of the body and the tissue fluids. In the present chapter we shall confine ourselves to the former function of the kidneys. The latter two will be discussed in chapter 11.

The basic functional unit in the kidney is the tiny structure known as the *nephron*, of which there are about one million in the two kidneys. The detailed histology of the nephron is beyond the scope of this work, but nevertheless it is essential that we note the more important details of its structure. Each nephron is intimately associated with a network of tiny bloodvessels.

In Figure 5.1 this association has been schematically portrayed by depicting the nephron itself as a straight tube (on the right-hand side of the drawing), and the bloodvessels by the crooked shaded tube, located at the left of the drawing. This drawing shows the blood-vessels making contact with the nephronal tube at two particular points. For the purposes of this discussion we may assume that different processes occur at each of these two points, the difference being due amongst other things, to differences in the permeability of the membranes concerned towards some of the constituents of the blood passing through the bloodvessels. Let us assume that at point A shown in the diagram, the membrane separating the blood in the bloodvessels from the interior of the nephron, has pores which are of such a size that it permits the passage through it of all the substances in blood, except the various blood cells and the large colloidal molecules, the blood plasma proteins. The porosity of this membrane thus permits a selective *filtration* of the constituents of blood to take place (process 1). Since the blood is in rapid circulation, it is essential that this filtration process also occurs rapidly. To this end it is aided by the high hydrostatic pressure under which the blood is circulating (i.e., the systemic blood pressure). Thus a large part of the circulating water together with its dissolved crystalloidal components is filtered at this particular part of the nephron, and passes from the bloodvessel into the interior of the nephronal tube.

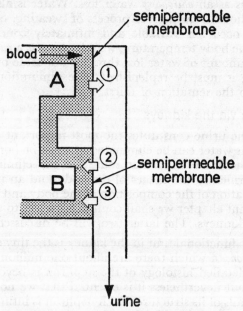

FIG. 5.1   Schematic representation of the working of a nephron.

Point B on the diagram is a second point of contact between the bloodvessels and the nephron. At this point the permeability of the dividing membrane is even more limited than at point A, allowing only water and a few small crystalloidal molecules or ions to pass through by the process of diffusion through the pores. The passage of most other larger molecules or ions occurs by means of the phenomenon known as *active transport*, and not through pores but across the membranes (process 2). Substances which are transported in this way are glucose, amino acids, and sodium ions together with other substances that are indispensable to the body. In this case they become *reabsorbed* into the blood stream, whilst any excess of these or waste products for which no transport system exists, are not returned to the blood.

As a result of the active reabsorption of the abovementioned substances a rapid building up of concentration occurs at the point to which they are being conveyed. This local high concentration of the substance concerned serves as a force for the *osmotic* attraction of water molecules, which as a result of this pass through pores in the membrane by the process of *osmosis* (process 3). The rest of the filtrate which consists of excess water, any excess of nutrient substances and waste products, is not reabsorbed and passes down the nephrons as *urine*. The nephrons empty into collecting ducts which open into the renal pelvis, where the urine is collected and passes into the urinary bladder via the ureters.

The exchange of fluid between the capillaries and the tissues of the body

The main functions of blood are to transport nutrients and oxygen to the tissue cells and to remove from their environment any waste products and carbon dioxide. This exchange of nutrients for waste products takes place in the myriad of capillaries present in the various tissues of the body. At the capillary level the blood and tissue fluids are separated by a *semipermeable membrane*, the pores of which permit the passage of crystalloids, but not the larger colloid molecules such as the plasma proteins. The following two phenomena underlie to a large extent the exchange of nutrients for waste products at the capillary level:

1. *Diffusion:* This phenomenon basically involves the movement of substances through pores large enough to accommodate them and the movement of fat soluble substances through membranes, from a high concentration of the particular substance to a low concentration. The blood arriving at the capillaries contains for instance a high concentration of oxygen and nutrients and a low concentration of various waste products including carbon dioxide. In the tissue

cells the concentration of oxygen and nutrients is generally low, since they are being utilized at a steady rate. The concentration of waste products in the tissues is higher than in the blood since they are being produced at a steady rate. The stage is thus set for the diffusion of these various products across the capillary membranes. Diffusion is the only way by which oxygen can leave the capillaries as it is transported by the red blood cells which always stay in the blood vessels.

2. *Fluid Exchange:* The blood in the vascular system circulates under pressure. This pressure, which we call the blood pressure, is induced by the pumping action of the heart, the distention of the arterial vessels, the elasticity of their walls, the viscosity of the blood itself and by no means least of all, the resistance offered to the flow of blood by the myriad of small-bore arterioles and capillaries. These combined effects exert a force upon the moving mass of blood, which is manifest as the blood pressure. Since blood is a fluid we often use a term borrowed from physics to describe this pressure, or force transmitted through it, notably *hydrostatic pressure.* The presence of this significant pressure implies at once a pressure difference between the blood in the capillaries and the tissue fluid outside. Since the pores in the capillaries are generally large enough to permit exit of water and crystalloidal substances but not the cells and larger protein molecules (colloids), outward movement of the former substances occurs, analogous to the process of filtration.

The presence of colloidal substances (proteins) inside the blood vessels exert an osmotic attraction on the water outside the blood vessels, as the two compartments are separated by a semipermeable membrane. The phenomenon of *osmosis* has been described in chapter 1. The force of attraction exerted by the solute particles is usually referred to as *osmotic pressure.* As in this case it is caused by colloidal substances in the plasma it is generally referred to as *colloid osmotic pressure.* Whilst the hydrostatic pressure favours an outward movement of fluid and solutes, the colloid osmotic pressure promotes a return of most of the fluid to the capillaries. More outward movement tends to occur at the arterial end of the capillaries where the hydrostatic pressure is high, while the colloid osmotic pressure favouring inward movement is most significant at the venous end of these tiny vessels, where the colloid osmotic pressure exceeds the hydrostatic pressure.

This to and fro movement of fluid favours the exchange of nutrients and waste products and regulates the composition of the tissue fluids. The fluid which is not reabsorbed at the venous end of the capillaries continues to bathe the tissue cells, and is ultimately taken up in the lymphatic system and rejoins the blood circulation when the lymph passes into this via the thoracic duct.

If for any reason the nett outward flow of fluid exceeds the inward return, an excessive amount of water accumulates in the tissues. This waterlogged state is known as *oedema* and develops for instance when the concentration of plasma proteins is lowered through disease or malnutrition. The lowered plasma protein level means a corresponding decrease in the colloid osmotic pressure, and a failure to attract the return of sufficient fluid at the venous end of the capillary bed. The same may happen when plasma proteins are lost via the urine in kidney disease, or when the venous hydrostatic pressure rises as in chronic heart disease.

Control of the water balance

In order to maintain a constant level of fluid in the body tissues, the amount of water taken in via the food and what we drink each day, plus the metabolic water, should equal the amount lost daily via the various avenues mentioned. Several important mechanisms are present in the body to ensure maintenance of the body water level.

In the first instance the intake of water is regulated by the thirst mechanism which involves complex nerve phenomena that are beyond the scope of this book. Water excretion can be controlled by the nervous regulation of the sweating mechanism, by the regulation of blood flow through the kidneys and by the regulation of water reabsorption in the nephrons. Nervous control rests largely in the autonomic nervous system, whilst control of reabsorption of water is largely a function of the two hormones, *anti-diuretic hormone* (ADH) and *aldosterone*. ADH increases the permeability of the nephronal membranes to water, thus promoting its reabsorption. Aldosterone on the other hand stimulates the active reabsorption of sodium ions. As explained earlier this phenomenon is coupled with an osmotic attraction of water, hence aldosterone stimulates water reabsorption in an indirect manner.

The dissociation and association of water

We noted in the previous chapter that water molecules (H_2O) are formed when two hydrogen atoms combine with one oxygen atom (Fig. 5.2). There are two bonds in the water molecules, one of which can occasionally break to provide hydrogen ions (H^+) and hydroxyl ions (OH^-) according to the equation:

$$H_2O \rightleftharpoons H^+ + OH^- \quad . . . . . (1)$$

The association between the oxygen and the remaining hydrogen in the hydroxyl radical is strong and is seldom broken. It seems as if once the oxygen has lost one of the two hydrogen ions, it retains the remaining one tenaciously. In fact this bond can only be broken if a

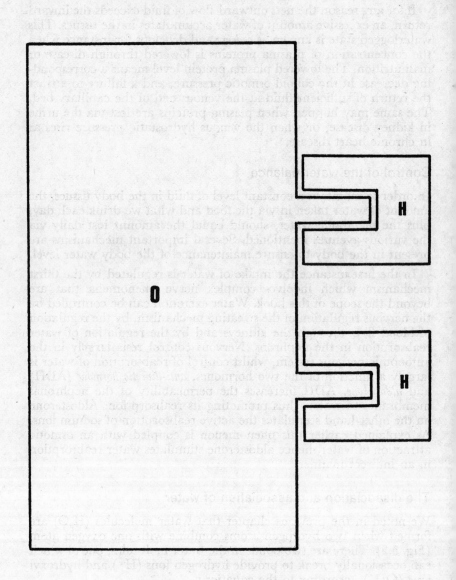

$$H_2O$$

FIG. 5.2   Schematic representation of a water molecule.

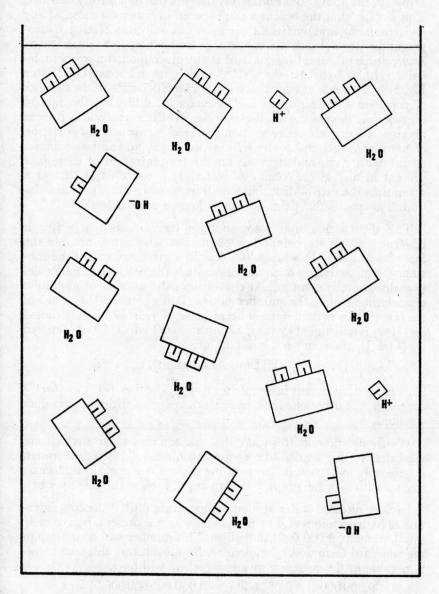

FIG. 5.3 Schematic representation of the dissociation of water.

strong electrical current is passed through water. The two-directional arrows in the above equation signify that the reaction is truly *reversible*. This implies that the reaction can proceed in either direction at any given moment, and that while water is continually dissociating, hydrogen and hydroxyl ions are continually associating to re-form water. Any volume of water thus contains at any given moment, water molecules (H_2O), hydrogen ions (H^+) and hydroxyl ions (OH^-) (see Fig. 5.3). The rate at which water dissociates depends on the number of water molecules present and occurs with difficulty, the rate of dissociation decreasing as the number of water molecules present decrease. As the rate of dissociation decreases, so the rate of association of hydrogen ions and hydroxyl ions increases, and this association occurs with ease, and depends on the concentration of these ions present in any given volume of water. It is conceivable that at a given time the rate of dissociation will be equal to the rate of association. This particular point in time is known as *equilibrium*.

The dissociation and association of compounds like water is governed by an important law of physical chemistry, notably the *law of mass action*. This law states that in a given volume of the substance, e.g., water, at a given temperature the number of molecules that dissociate is constant. At equilibrium the number of molecules dissociating equals the number of associating ions and in terms of the law of mass action, if the concentration of hydrogen ions (denoted by $[H^+]$) is multiplied by the concentration of hydroxyl ions (denoted by $[OH^-]$), the result is a constant, or,

$$[H^+] \times [OH^-] = k \text{ (a constant)}. \ldots (2)$$

This expression means in simple terms that if either $[H^+]$ or $[OH^-]$ decreases, the other one must increase to keep the arithmetic product constant.

We should note at this stage that the square brackets which are used denote the words, "the concentration of". This concentration is generally expressed in terms of the mole, i.e. the gram molecular mass per litre (or the gram atomic mass per litre, as the case may be).

In pure distilled water at room temperature (20°C) the concentration of hydrogen ions and hydroxyl ions which is present, is extremely small, namely, 0,000 0001 mole/litre. This number can be written in the standard form as 10^{-7} mole/litre. By substituting this concentration value in the equation given above, we will have

$$0,000\,000\,1 \times 0,000\,000\,1 = 0,000\,000\,000\,000\,01 \quad \text{or}$$
$$10^{-7} \times 10^{-7} = 10^{-14}$$

Thus, when water dissociates, it always does so producing an equal number of hydrogen ions and hydroxyl ions. At room temperature the production of these ions proceeds at a constant rate. The number 10^{-14} is known as the dissociation constant for water at room temperature.

The concept of pH

Since hydrogen ions are extremely reactive they can exert a profound influence on chemical processes taking place in their environment. This is especially true for living cells and it follows then that it is of vital importance to regulate the hydrogen ion concentration inside the cells and in tissue fluids within narrow limits.

We noted in the previous chapter that acids such as sulphuric acid or phosphoric acid dissociate in aqueous solution to yield hydrogen ions and a negatively charged radical. In terms of what has been said above the concentration of hydrogen ions in the solution therefore increases above the value of 10^{-7} mole/litre. If the expression (2) is to hold, then the concentration of hydroxyl ions in these solutions of acids must decrease correspondingly below the value of 10^{-7} mole/litre.

A solution in which the concentration of hydrogen ions is in excess of 10^{-7} mole/litre is known as an *acidic* solution. Conversely if the concentration of hydroxyl ions is greater than 10^{-7} mole/litre (which means that $[H^+]$ will be less than this value) we speak of an *alkaline* solution.

The numerical values used above, e.g. 10^{-7} mole/litre, are cumbersome when it comes to expressing the hydrogen ion concentration, for instance the expression $[H^+] = 10^{-7}$ mole/litre, reads, "the hydrogen ion concentration equals ten to the power of minus seven mole/litre". The pH system is used to simplify expression of statements like the above one to a remarkable degree. We merely replace the previous statement by the simple expression

$$pH = 7$$

where pH is taken to mean "the hydrogen ion concentration" and seven is the negative power of ten in the term 10^{-7}. It is this power which is the most meaningful in expressions of this nature, so we use it as a whole number, whilst bearing in mind what we mean by it. By the same token, $[H^+] = 10^{-3}$ or $[H^+] = 10^{-12}$ can be written as $pH = 3$ or $pH = 12$ respectively.

We must bear in mind that 10^{-3} (or 1/1 000) is a larger number than 10^{-4} (or 1/10 000). In other words the smaller the value of the negative power, the larger is the number, the smaller the pH value, the greater is the hydrogen ion concentration and *vice versa*. A *pH of less than 7* indicates an *acidic* solution, while a *pH of greater than 7* indicates an *alkaline* solution. A *pH of 7* indicates *neutrality* in the absolute sense.

When we consider the hydrogen ion concentration of body fluids, neutrality of these does not coincide with the absolute value of 7, but rather with the pH values 7,3 - 7,4 i.e. the fluids of the body are slightly alkaline. In health the pH of the body fluids is maintained within these very narrow limits. A fall in pH to a value of 7,2 represents a considerable increase in the hydrogen ion concentration and one which is sufficient to cause serious disturbances of cell function. If the pH of body fluids falls to 7, the increase in hydrogen ion concentration is such that cell function is catastrophically impaired, and coma and death result. We speak of such a condition as an *acidosis*. An acidosis is a frequent complication of diseases like diabetes mellitus, in which excessive amounts of acids are produced in the body.

If, on the other hand, the pH of body fluids rises above 7,6, the results can be equally catastrophic and a state of *alkalosis* arises.

The dissociation of substances in aqueous solutions

A great variety of substances dissociate in aqueous solution to yield cations and anions. Since such solutions conduct electricity, such substances are referred to as *electrolytes*. We have encountered the following examples so far:

$$NaCl \rightleftharpoons Na^+ + Cl^-$$
$$KBr \rightleftharpoons K^+ + Br^-$$
$$NH_4Cl \rightleftharpoons NH_4^+ + Cl^-$$

These salts, sodium chloride, potassium bromide and ammonium chloride, dissociate fully in aqueous solution and are consequently referred to as *strong electrolytes*.

Carbonic acid can dissociate yielding hydrogen ions and bicarbonate ions according to the equation

$$H_2CO_3 \rightleftharpoons H^+ + HCO_3^-$$

As in the case of water this compound dissociates poorly and solutions of carbonic acid contain relatively large amounts of undissociated acid and few hydrogen or bicarbonate ions. Compounds which dissociate poorly are referred to as *weak electrolytes*.

We can see therefore that different electrolytes do not all dissociate to the same extent in aqueous solution. The degree of dissociation is indicated by the numerical value of the *dissociation constant* for the compound concerned. The greater this value is, the greater is the degree of dissociation. When hydrochloric acid (HCl) is dissolved in water, the following occurs:

$$HCl \rightleftharpoons H^+ + Cl^-$$

Since on dissociation hydrochloric acid liberates hydrogen ions the concentration of the latter will increase the value of those normally present in water. The solution will therefore become acidic. On the other hand when sodium hydroxide (NaOH) is dissolved in water the following occurs:

$$NaOH \rightleftharpoons Na^+ + OH^-$$

The excess hydroxyl (OH⁻) ions will actually bind with and remove some hydrogen ions and the solution will become alkaline. When solutions of hydrochloric acid and sodium hydroxide are mixed the following set of reactions will take place:

$$HCl \rightleftharpoons H^+ + Cl^-$$
$$NaOH \rightleftharpoons Na^+ + OH^-$$
$$H^+ + OH^- \rightleftharpoons H_2O$$
$$Na^+ + Cl^- \rightleftharpoons NaCl$$

The four reactions can be taken together in one single reaction, namely:

$$HCl + NaOH \rightleftharpoons H_2O + NaCl$$

This final equation does not tell us that HCl or NaOH dissociate fully when dissolved in water, nor does it tell us that the water and sodium chloride form by the association of ions. We know that the first mentioned compounds are strong electrolytes and we know that sodium and chloride ions have a strong affinity for one another. We also know that when hydrogen and hydroxyl ions occur in solution they will associate to form water, and water dissociates poorly. The chances are excellent that the products of the reaction will be water and sodium chloride. We thus accept these facts and write down the simplified equation.

The products of the reaction between an acid (in this case hydrochloric acid) and an alkali (in this case sodium hydroxide) are a salt (in this case sodium chloride) and water. If we mix hydrochloric acid and sodium hydroxide in the molecular proportions indicated by the equation, they will exactly *neutralise* one another. We can calculate the proportions required by calculating the molecular masses of the compounds concerned with the aid of the periodic table (which supplies us with the atomic masses of hydrogen, chlorine, sodium and oxygen). According to the equation, 36g of HCl are required to neutralise 40g of NaOH. The products of this reaction will be 18g of water and 58g of sodium chloride. The equation provides us with the proportions of the reacting substances in terms of their molecular masses. Although in this example we have expressed these proportions in grams, we could just as well have done so in micrograms, milligrams or even kilograms. The proportions still hold good, no matter what the units may be.

In terms of what has been said so far an acid is any substance which in solution yields hydrogen ions, and an alkali is a substance which removes hydrogen ions from the solution, since it yields hydroxyl ions which readily associate with hydrogen ions to form the poorly dissociated water molecule. Acids or alkalis may be weak or strong depending on the degree of dissociation which they exhibit in solution. *Strong acids* are for instance hydrochloric acid (HCl), sulphuric acid (H_2SO_4), nitric acid (HNO_3) and orthophosphoric acid (H_3PO_4). Some examples of *weak acids* are carbonic acid (H_2CO_3) and boric acid (H_3BO_4). Sodium, potassium and ammonium hydroxides (NaOH, KOH and NH_4OH) are all *strong alkalis*, while calcium and magnesium hydroxides ($Ca(OH)_2$ and $Mg(OH)_2$) are *weak* alkalis.

Salts which are formed during the reaction between an acid and an alkali will dissociate fully in solution if one or both of the original reactants was a strong acid or base, as the case may be. Where both were weak in this respect, the resulting salt will be one which dissociates poorly in solution.

Salts are generally named according to the cation which is present in the salt molecule (e.g. sodium, potassium or calcium) and the anion derived from the acid which was concerned in the formation of the salt, e.g.

chlorides from hydrochloric acid (anion: Cl^-)
sulphates from sulphuric acid (anion: $SO_4^=$)
nitrates from nitric acid (anion: NO_3^-)
bromides from hydrobromic acid (anion: Br^-)
carbonates from carbonic acid (anion: $CO_3^=$)
bicarbonates from carbonic acid (anion: HCO_3^-)

Acids such as sulphuric (H_2SO_4), carbonic (H_2CO_3), and orthophosphoric (H_3PO_4) acids, all of which contain more than one ionisable hydrogen atom can yield more than one type of salt, e.g. sulphates or bisulphates ($SO_4^=$ or HSO_4^-), carbonates or bicarbonates ($CO_3^=$ or HCO_3^-) and so on. Orthophosphoric acid with its three ionisable hydrogen atoms can form three types of salt, notably dihydrogen phosphates ($H_2PO_4^-$), monohydrogen phosphates ($HPO_4^=$) and basic phosphates ($PO_4^\equiv$). Only the first two types are of any physiological importance. Salts such as bicarbonates, bisulphates and dihydrogen phosphates can be regarded as *acidic salts* since the anion can dissociate further in the following way:

$$H_2PO_4^- \rightleftharpoons H^+ + HPO_4^=$$
$$HCO_3^- \rightleftharpoons H^+ + CO_3^=$$
and $$HSO_4^- \rightleftharpoons H^+ + SO_4^=$$

Carbonates and bicarbonates are interesting salts, since they can act as alkalis and neutralize acids as follows:

$$Na_2CO_3 + 2HCl \rightleftharpoons 2NaCl + H_2O + CO_2$$
$$NaHCO_3 + HCl \rightleftharpoons NaCl + H_2O + CO_2$$

When an acid reacts with a carbonate or bicarbonate, the reaction products are always a salt, water and carbon dioxide.

Salts can also be formed when an acid acts upon a metallic element, e.g. zinc chloride is formed when zinc and hydrochloric acid react with one another:

$$Zn + 2HCl = ZnCl_2 + H_2$$

Buffers

A buffer solution has the power to resist changes in its pH following the addition of strong acids or bases. It usually contains a weak acid and a salt of that acid, or a weak alkali and a salt of that alkali. Let us assume that we have a solution containing carbonic acid (H_2CO_3) and sodium bicarbonate ($NaHCO_3$). These two compounds will ionize poorly as follows:

$$H_2CO_3 \rightleftharpoons H^+ + HCO_3^-$$
$$NaHCO_3 \rightleftharpoons Na^+ + HCO_3^-$$

If we add a strong acid such as HCl to the solution, the following will occur:

$$HCl \rightleftharpoons H^+ + Cl^-$$
$$H^+ + HCO_3^- \rightleftharpoons H_2CO_3$$
$$Na^+ + Cl^- \rightleftharpoons NaCl$$

More of the poorly dissociated carbonic acid forms, together with the salt, sodium chloride and little change has occurred in the hydrogen ion concentration of the solution. If we add a strong alkali like NaOH to the solution, the following will occur:

$$NaOH \rightleftharpoons Na^+ + OH^-$$
$$Na^+ + HCO_3^- \rightleftharpoons NaHCO_3$$
$$OH^- + H^+ \rightleftharpoons H_2O$$

Poorly dissociated water and the salt sodium bicarbonate form, and once more little change in the hydrogen ion concentration of the solution is brought about. Buffer mixtures are of great physiological importance and are concerned with the maintenance of the pH of body fluids. This topic will be pursued further in chapter 11, in more detail.

Indicators

The presence of acids and alkalis in a solution can be revealed by the use of *indicators*. These are certain dyes that assume characteristic colours in acidic and alkaline solutions, as shown in the table below.

Indicator	Colour in acid solution	Colour in alkaline solution
Litmus	red	blue
Phenolphthalein	colourless	red
Methyl orange	red	yellow

Should we wish to measure the acid or alkaline content of a solution, we can do so by *titration*. This involves the addition of acid or alkali to known volumes of the solution to be tested until the solution is exactly neutralized. An indicator is used to show up the endpoint of the titration. The amount of acid or alkali used to bring about neutrality can then be used to calculate the hydrogen ion content of the solution being tested. Electronic devices, known as pH-meters, are in common use to determine the hydrogen ion concentration of solutions. More elegant devices are available for the direct measurement of the bicarbonate content and the pH of samples of blood and other tissue fluids.

Equivalent mass

It is usual to express concentration in terms of mass per unit volume, the litre being the unit of volume generally selected for chemical work. Another very meaningful system much used in biochemical and physiological work is to express concentrations in terms of the equivalent mass of a substance. This is defined as the mass of a substance which will *combine with or displace one gram of hydrogen*. Let us consider for the moment the equation

$$H_2O \rightleftharpoons H^+ + OH^-$$

This tells us that one hydrogen ion combines with one hydroxyl ion. If we work out the masses of the reactants, it will be apparent that 1 gram of hydrogen ions combines with 17 grams of hydroxyl ions to form 18 grams of water. Thus the equivalent masses of the hydroxyl ions and water are 17 and 18 grams respectively. If we consider the equation

$$HCl \rightleftharpoons H^+ + Cl^-$$

it is apparent that the equivalent masses of hydrochloric acid and chloride ions are 36 and 35 respectively.

From the equation

$$NaOH \rightleftharpoons Na^+ + OH^-$$

we can deduce that the equivalent masses of sodium and sodium hydroxide are 23 and 40 grams respectively, as one sodium ion replaces one hydrogen ion in water.

The equation

$$NaOH + HCl \rightleftharpoons NaCl + H_2O$$

tells us that one equivalent of sodium hydroxide combines with one equivalent of hydrochloric acid to produce one equivalent mass of sodium chloride, and one of water. In all these examples the equivalent mass is numerically equal to the molecular mass. The situation is, however, slightly different in the following instance:

$$H_2SO_4 \rightleftharpoons 2H^+ + SO_4^=$$

In this case one sulphate ion combines with two hydrogen ions *or* one molecule of sulphuric acid yields two hydrogen ions. The equivalent mass of the sulphate ion and of sulphuric acid is the half of their respective molecular masses. The equivalent mass of an atom is readily calculated by *dividing its atomic mass by its valency*.

It is common practice in biochemical and physiological work to use submultiples of the equivalent mass of a particular ion or compound, e.g. the milli-equivalent mass. This is one-thousandth of the equivalent mass and when it is used, concentrations are generally given as *milli-equivalents per litre*.

Molarity and normality

Concentrations may be expressed in terms of *molarity*. A molar (1M) solution of a substance contains the molecular mass of the substance expressed in grams, in one litre of solution. A 1M solution of HCl therefore contains 38g HCl per litre, and 1M H_2SO_4 is a solution containing 98g of H_2SO_4 per litre. Fractions or multiples are often used, e.g. 0,5 molar, 2M, 0,1M and so on.

Alternately concentrations can be expressed in terms of *normality*. A normal (1N) solution of a substance contains one gram equivalent mass of the substance in one litre of solution. Fractions or multiples of the equivalent mass dissolved in 1 litre of solution are indicated as 2N, 10N, 0,1N, 0,001N and so on.

CHAPTER 6

Carbon-containing Compounds

Carbon-containing compounds form a large part of living matter; the carbon usually being combined with elements such as oxygen, hydrogen, nitrogen, phosphorus, sulphur and in a few cases with metallic elements such as magnesium, iron, manganese, and so on. The most important groups of these substances occurring in the body are carbohydrates, proteins and fats. The hydrocarbons are a simpler group of compounds. Although they are present only in traces in some body tissues, they will be discussed in this chapter since a knowledge of them is in many ways essential to an understanding of the more complex compounds.

Hydrocarbons

Hydrocarbons are the simplest of the carbon-containing substances, their basic structures being composed only of carbon and hydrogen. They can in a sense, be considered as the parent substances of a great variety of compounds which can be formed by substituting various *functional groups* for one or more of the hydrogen atoms in their molecules. These groups include *hydroxyl* ($-OH$), *aldehyde* ($-CHO$), *ketone* or *carbonyl* ($-CO$), *carboxyl* ($-COOH$), *ether* ($-O-$) or *amino-groups* ($-NH_2$). Hydrocarbons can be divided into two main groups depending on the way in which the constituent atoms are arranged in the molecule, namely, *aliphatic* and *cyclic* hydrocarbons.

Aliphatic hydrocarbons

Aliphatic carbons consist of open chains of carbon atoms. The chains are generally unbranched in which case the compounds are called normal (n—) hydrocarbons. In certain instances the chains may be branched. If the bonds between all the carbon atoms are simple covalent bonds the molecules are considered as *saturated*, and are known as *alkanes*. If, however, some of the bonds are double or triple covalent bonds the compounds are known as *unsaturated* hydrocarbons, and termed *alkenes* and *alkynes* respectively.

Alkanes contain a series of carbon atoms joined by normal covalent bonds. There is an even number of hydrogen atoms present in each member of the series and this can always be calculated by doubling

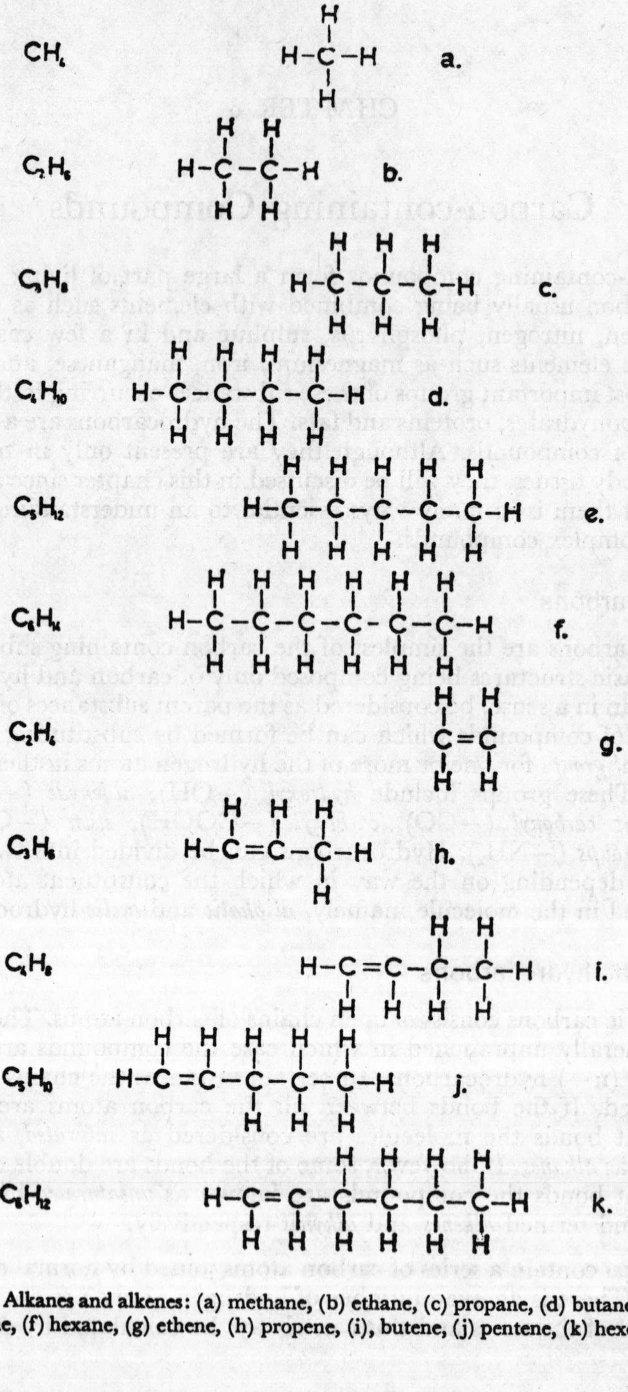

CH_4 — (a)

C_2H_6 — (b)

C_3H_8 — (c)

C_4H_{10} — (d)

C_5H_{12} — (e)

C_6H_{14} — (f)

C_2H_4 — (g)

C_3H_6 — (h)

C_4H_8 — (i)

C_5H_{10} — (j)

C_6H_{12} — (k)

Fig. 6.1 Alkanes and alkenes: (a) methane, (b) ethane, (c) propane, (d) butane, (e) pentane, (f) hexane, (g) ethene, (h) propene, (i), butene, (j) pentene, (k) hexene.

the number of carbon atoms present and adding two. If, for example, a hydrocarbon contains three carbon atoms, the number of hydrogen atoms is

$$(2 \times 3) + 2 = 8$$

hence the general formula for these compounds may be expressed as

$C_nH_{2n} + 2$ where n is always a whole number.

The following are some of the best known alkanes: methane (CH_4), ethane (C_2H_6), propane (C_3H_8), butane (C_4H_{10}), pentane (C_5H_{12}), and hexane (C_6H_{14}) (Fig. 6.1). The series continues through to compounds containing thirty or more carbon atoms. The first five of the above-mentioned substances are gases some of which are used in domestic heating appliances. The next few in the series are liquids and form an important part of petroleum. Chains containing more than ten carbon atoms make up part of heavy oils or waxlike substances and are encountered as kerosene (paraffin), lubricating oils and greases.

Alkenes contain one or more double bonds and have the general formula $C:H_2$: (i.e., they have twice as many hydrogen atoms as carbon atoms).

Examples are: ethene (C_2H_4), propene (C_3H_6), butene (C_4H_8), pentene (C_5H_{10}), hexene (C_6H_{12}) (Fig. 6.1), and so on. These substances are generally very reactive gases as a result of the presence of double bonds.

Alkynes have one or more triple bonds and have the general formula $C_nH_{2n}-2$. The simplest member of the series is acetylene. Like all alkines it is a very reactive gas which burns in the presence of oxygen to produce an intensely hot flame. Flames of this nature are used for welding or for cutting metal plates.

Cyclic hydrocarbons

Cyclic hydrocarbons are characterised by having their carbon atoms joined to form a cyclic or ring structure. The most important rings contain five (Fig. 6.2a), or six carbon atoms (Fig. 6.2b). When the molecule contains only one such ring we speak of a monocyclic strutture (Fig. 6.2a and b, 6.3a and b). When more than one ring is present we speak of di- (Fig. 6.3d, Fig. 6.3c), tri- (Fig. 6.3e, f, g), tetra- (Fig. 6.2d and Fig 6.3g) and pentacyclic structures. Such com. pounds are collectively called polycyclic hydrocarbons. These ring structures can be saturated (Fig. 6.2) or unsaturated (Fig. 6.3). Saturated cyclic hydrocarbons are called *alicyclic hydrocarbons* or *cycloalkanes* while unsaturated ones are generally referred to as *aromatic hydrocarbons* or *cycloalkenes*. A number of alicyclic hydrocarbons are

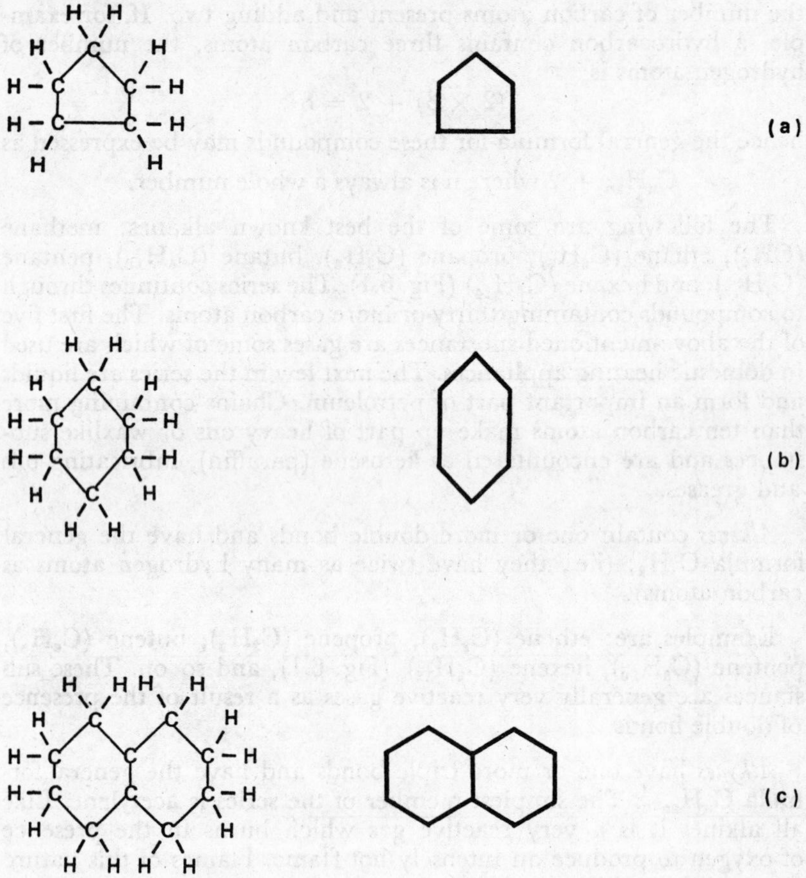

(a)

(b)

(c)

(d)

Fig. 6.2 Alicyclic hydrocarbons or Cycloalkanes: (a) cyclopropane, (b) cyclohexane, (c) decalin, (d) cyclopentanoperhydrophenantrene. (a) and (b) are mono-, (c) is a di- and (d) is a tetracyclic compound.

of great importance to the body, particularly the type exemplified by Fig. 6.2d. This ring system is present in biologically important compounds like the vitamins D and their precursors, cholesterol, the bile salts, the sex hormones and the hormones of the adrenal gland. This particular ring system is often referred to as a *steroid* ring system and hence the compounds just mentioned are often loosely referred to as steroids or steroidal compounds.

It should be evident from Fig. 6.2 that the drawing of a complete molecule of a polycyclic hydrocarbon can be a time-consuming task if all carbon and hydrogen atoms are to be shown. To obviate this it is common practice to indicate the skeleton of carbon atoms only (Figs. 6.2 and 6.3). If in addition other functional groups (such as $-CH_3$, $-COOH$, $-OH$), are present they are shown in full (Fig. 6.3b), attached to the appropriate carbon atom in the ring system.

Some aromatic hydrocarbons are depicted in Fig. 6.3. Many of these substances are of great importance. Benzene (C_6H_6), toluene ($C_6H_5CH_3$) and xylene ($C_6H_4(CH_3)_2$, are important solvents. Various derivatives of these include aspirin, colouring agents, insecticides, plastics and explosives. The sources of many of these substances are coal, from which they can be obtained by distillation, and shale oil.

Other ring systems are encountered in nature that include oxygen, nitrogen and sulphur atoms as part of the ring. Strictly speaking these substances are not hydrocarbons, but they behave similarly to the latter in many respects and among them are many substances of biological, pharmacological and industrial importance. They are known as *heterocyclic* compounds and most substances in our body having ring systems are of this type. The properties of this group of compounds varies to a very great extent from compound to compound. One of the most important common properties is the presence of unshared pairs of electrons on the nitrogen atoms, conferring on these compounds basic properties. Examples of this group are shown in Fig. 6.4. Note that in the skeleton structures only the non-carbon atoms are indicated. In some instances several ring systems may be joined by carbon atoms outside the ring concerned, in which case these carbon atoms are indicated (Fig. 6.41). A large compound ring structure like that of porphin (Fig. 6.41) is called a *macrocyclic* ring system.

Derivatives of hydrocarbons

As mentioned earlier various functional groups can be attached to the hydrocarbon molecules and substitute for hydrogen atoms. These groups include halogens (see chapter 3) forming *halogen derivatives*, hydroxyl ($-OH$) group forming *alcohols* and *phenols*, aldehyde

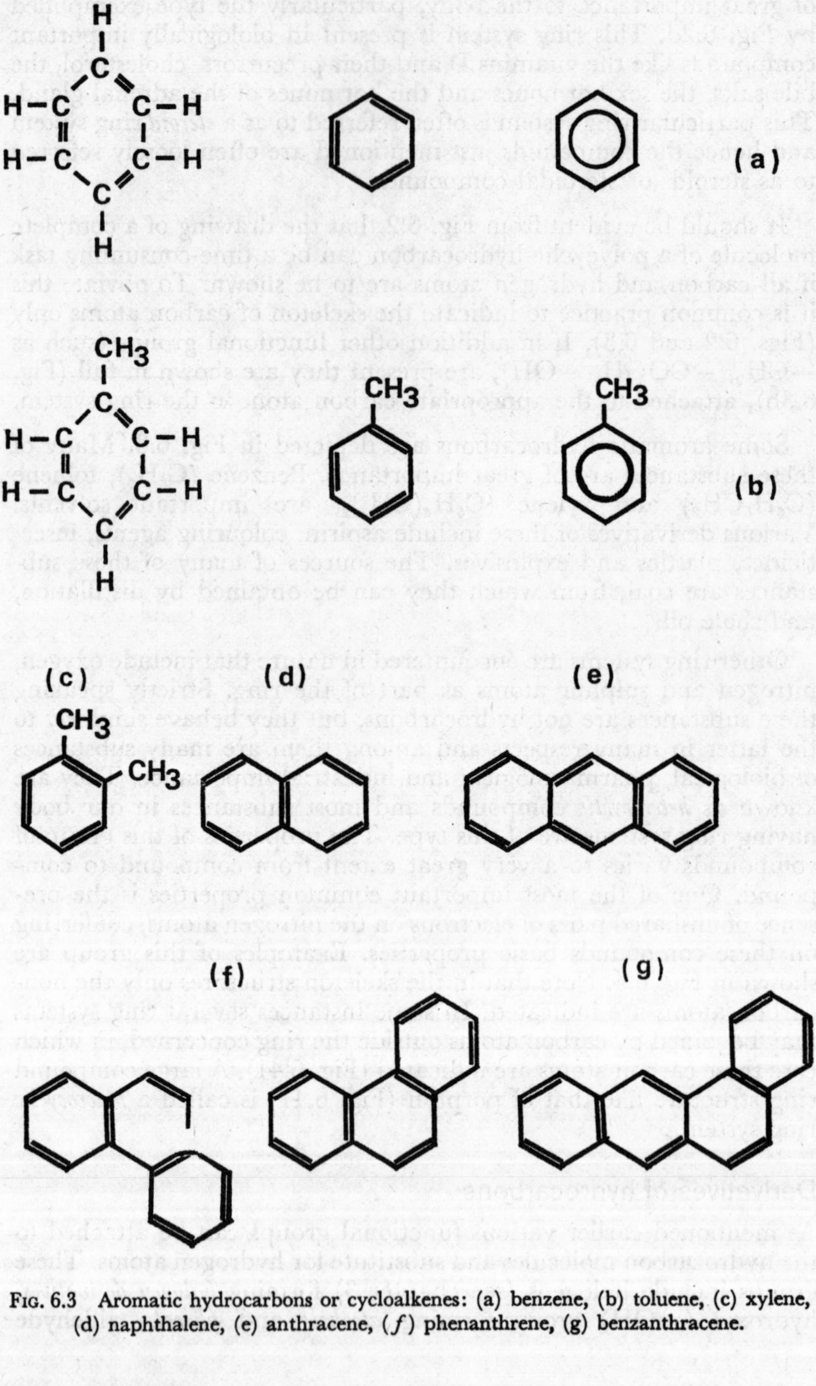

Fig. 6.3 Aromatic hydrocarbons or cycloalkenes: (a) benzene, (b) toluene, (c) xylene, (d) naphthalene, (e) anthracene, (*f*) phenanthrene, (g) benzanthracene.

($-$CHO) groups forming *aldehydes*, carbonyl groups ($-$ CO) form-ing *ketones*, carboxyl group ($-$COOH) forming *carboxylic acids* and so on. Examples of *halogen derivatives* are the well-known solvents methyl, chloride (CH_3Cl), dichoromethane (CH_2Cl_2), chloroform ($CHCl_3$) and carbon tetrachloride (CCl_4). Chloroform was used as an anaesthetic agent, but its use was discontinued because of its dangerous side-effects. The compound iodoform (CHI_3) is still used to a certain extent as an antiseptic agent. Complex halogen deriva-tives such as dichloro-tetrafluoro-ethane ($C_2Cl_2F_4$) and monochloro-difluoro-methane ($CHClF_2$) are used in domestic refrigerators under the name of "Freon".

Alcohols and phenols

Alcohols have antiseptic properties and are often used as solvents. Some of the simpler ones are freely miscible with water. Many of them are inflammable, and caution is therefore required when using them. The most important alcohols for medical purposes are metha-nol (CH_3OH), ethanol (C_2H_5OH), isopropanol (C_3H_7OH), ethyle-neglycol ($C_2H_4(OH_2)$, and glycerol ($C_3H_5(OH)_3$). *Methanol* is the simplest of the alcohols. It is extremely poisonous causing blindness, muscle paralysis and death if taken by mouth. It forms part of methylated spirits which is commonly used as a solvent or as a fuel for spirit burners.

Ethanol is the product that we commonly call "alcohol". It has been used as a beverage from the earliest times, being obtained by the fermentation of sugars and starches. Fermentation is catalyzed by the enzymes present in yeast. Industrially ethanol is obtained from the hydrocarbon, ethane, the product being a 96% pure alco-hol. Absolute or 100% ethanol is very expensive for two reasons. Firstly it is costly to eliminate the 4% of impurities and secondly by universal agreement very high fiscal duties are added to its price. It can be obtained in a cheap form, the so-called methylated spirits to which methanol, pyridine and violet colouring matter have been added making it completely unpalatable and dangerous for internal use. In any event pure ethanol itself is a dangerous drug if taken in large amounts having many harmful effects apart from the well-known problems of intoxication and alcoholism. When taken in small amounts it is a severe nervous tissue depressant despite its apparent stimulant effects. Use is made of its solvent properties in the preparation of medicines such as *tinctures* made from products of natural origin. Tincture of iodine is a solution of iodine in ethanol, much used as an antiseptic for external application.

Glycerol, often called glycerine, is a very important component of animal and plant fats and therefore of our bodies as well. Commer-cially it is obtained as the by-product of soap production and apart

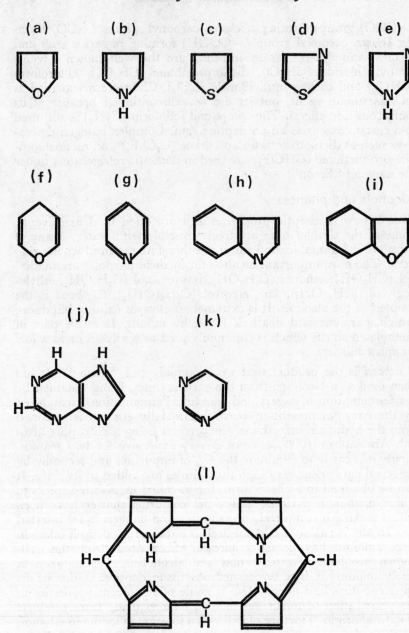

Fig. 6.4 Heterocyclic compounds: (a) furan, (b) pyrrole, (c) thiophene, (d) thiazole, (e) imidazole, (f) pyran, (g) pyridine, (h) indole, (i) coumarone, (j) purine, (k) pyrimidine, and (l) porphin.

from its use as a solvent in pharmacy it is extensively used as a component of beauty preparations and in the manufacture of explosives like nitroglycerine. It is a heavy, viscous and colourless liquid.

Phenols are alcohols derived from the aromatic hydrocarbon series (Fig. 6.5a). These compounds are very poisonous with strong antiseptic properties. The simplest of them is *phenol*, a pink, crystalline compound, often referred to as carbolic acid.

The *cresols* are a group of phenols containing methyl groups in addition to the functional hydroxyl groups (Fig. 6.5b). They are well-known antiseptic agents and are obtainable in soapy solutions like "lysol" or as commercial "dips".

Aldehydes and ketones

Aldehydes are strong reducing agents, are poisonous and have sharp, irritating, unpleasant odours. The simple aldehydes, formaldehyde (HCHO) and acetaldehyde are gases, while others are liquids or solids. Formalin, a 40% solution of formaldehyde is used as a fixative for tissue specimens, as a preservative of such specimens, and as a disinfectant. Acetaldehyde is used as the parent compound for the industrial synthesis of many other compounds. One of its derivatives, *chloralhydrate*, is used as a sedative or soporific (sleep-producing agent).

The best known *ketone* is *acetone*, $(CH_3)_2CO$. It is used in the production of cosmetics such as nail varnish remover. It is also found as an abnormal constituent of urine during severe fasting and in cases of diabetes mellitus. In the latter case it has diagnostic significance.

Carboxylic acids

Carboxylic acids are of great physiological and biochemical importance. This group includes the fatty acids, keto acids, cyclic acids and amino acids. In many of these cases there are other functional groups, such as carbonyl, hydroxyl or amino-groups present apart from the carboxyl groups which confer acidic properties on the molecule.

Fatty acids or *monobasic acids* form a homologous series of aliphatic hydrocarbon derivatives each of them differing from the previous one by $-CH_2$ and contain a single carboxyl group. The origin of their name is due to the fact that they are present in animal and vegetable fat, usually in conjunction with glycerol. Certain of them are also formed during fat metabolism in the body. Fatty acids can be saturated acids, containing only simple covalent bonds in their molecules, such as formic acid $(H \cdot COOH)$, acetic acid $(CH_3 \cdot COOH)$, propionic acid $(C_2H_5 \cdot COOH)$, butyric acid (C_3H_7COOH), palmitic acid $(C_{15}H_{31}COOH)$, and so on. Others are unsaturated such as

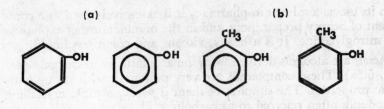

oleic acid $(C_{17}H_{33}COOH)$, linoleic acid $(C_{17}H_{31}COOH)$, linolenic acid $(C_{17}H_{29}COOH)$, and arachidonic acid $(C_{19}H_{35}COOH)$. These are physiologically very important compounds and the latter three are frequently referred to as essential fatty acids since the body does not synthesize them in adequate amounts. They are probably precursors of the group of hormiones known as the prostaglandns, as well as being important components of cell membranes.

Dibasic and *tribasic acids* contain two and three carboxyl groups, respectively. Some of them are important metabolic intermediary substances. Examples are succinic acid, tartraic acid and citric acid (Fig. 6.5). The latter two also contain a hydroxyl group in their molecules and are called hydroxy-acids.

Keto acids carry a carbonyl group in addition to the carboxyl group. They are important intermediary metabolic products, e.g. acetoacetic acid and pyruvic acid.

*Cyclic acid s*contain a ring system in addition to the acrboxyl group. The two most important of these substances, benzoic acid $(C_6H_5.(COOH))$ and salicyclic acid (Fig. 6.5) are used as preservatives in the food industry. Aspirin (acetyl-salicyclic acid) is a derivative of salicyclic acid.

Amino acids have an amino $(—NH_2)$ group in addition to their carboxyl group and have the general formula

$$H$$
$$|$$
$$R — C — COOH$$
$$|$$
$$NH_2$$

R being any one of a number of carbon containing radicals. Amino acids are important building stones for the *proteins*. These in turn are the most important components of tissues. There are about twenty-three different amino acids which occur in proteins and about another thirty exist as metabolic intermediary products in animal and plant tissues. Examples of amino acids are glycine, alanine, phenylalanine and tyrosine (Fig. 6.5). In the proteins, the amino acids are linked to one another by *peptide linkages* to form a chain characteristic of the protein molecule. Several hundreds or thousands of them can be present in a protein. These substances consequently have a very high molecular mass.

The ability of amino acids to combine with one another depends upon the fact that the amino group has strong basic properties and the carboxyl group has strong acidic properties. A substance wihch has both acidic and basic groups is said to be *amphoteric* or is an *ampholyte* and when both groups are ionized simultaneously, the ion is referred to as a "*zwitterion*" (from the German zwitter, a hybrid or hermaphrodite). The carboxyl group ionizes by releasing a hydrogen ion, while the amino group takes up a proton (hydrogen ion) to become $-NH_3^+$. The dissociation and association concerned can be represented as follows:

$$\underset{\underset{COOH}{|}}{\overset{\overset{R}{|}}{H_2N-C-H}} \rightleftharpoons \underset{\underset{COO^-}{|}}{\overset{\overset{R}{|}}{H_3N^+-C-H}} + H^+$$

Esters, Ethers and Amines

Esters are solids or liquids which form when a carboxylic acid combines with simple aliphatic or aromatic alcohol according to the equation

$$R - OH + H O \cdot OC - R_1 \rightleftharpoons R - O - O - C - R_1 + H_2O$$

There are three groups of esters that are of industrial, domestic or physiological importance:

1. Esters of fatty acids with simple alcohols. These are found in many fruits and flowers, and are responsible for their characteristic odours and flavours. They are also used as artificial flavouring agents, e.g. ethyl acetate has a flavour reminiscent of apples, pears and peaches, while that of ethyl butyrate resembles pineapples or bananas. Many esters, like ethyl acetate, for instance, are widely used as solvents.

2. Esters of glycerol with medium or long chain fatty acids. These are called *neutral fats* and will be discussed later under the heading of Lipids.

3. Esters of long chain or alicyclic alcohols with long chain fatty acids. These are generally known as *waxes*. In plants and animals these substances protect surfaces such as those of leaves, skin, and the ear drum against drying out and against the penetration of foreign particles. Waxes are also used in the manufacture of candles, floor and shoe polishes, soaps, ointments and similar medicinal agents.

Ethers are formed when two alcohols combine with one another in the presence of a dehydrating agent according to the equation

$$R - OH + HO - R_1 \rightleftharpoons R - O - R_1 + H_2O$$

R and R_1 may be the same radicals thus providing a simple ether or different radicals thus giving rise to a compound or mixed ether. The best known is diethylether ($C_2H_5 \cdot O \cdot C_2H_5$ generally known as ether) formerly much used as an anaesthetic. Ethers are used as solvents for a wide variety of fatty and other substances.

The *amines* are derived from the hydrocarbons by the substitution of one or more amino groups for hydrogen atoms. The hydrocarbons concerned, and thus also the amines derived from them, may be aliphatic, aromatic, alicyclic or heterocyclic compounds. A specific type of amine, the so-called quarternary amines are strong detergents and good disinfectants. These substances contain a positively charged nitrogen atom to which are bound four similar or different radicals as follows:

$$R_3 - \overset{\overset{\displaystyle R}{|}}{\underset{\underset{\displaystyle R_2}{|}}{N^+}} - R_1$$

Some simple cyclic amines are used in the production of a great variety of dyes and medicinal substances. Important examples of these are aniline $(C_6H_5NH_2)$, toluidine $(C_6H_4CH_3NH_2)$, xylidene $(C_6H_3(CH_3)_2NH_2)$ and naphthalene $(C_{10}H_7NH_2)$.

A few amines, like putrescine $(H_2N-(CH_2)_4-NH_2)$ and cadaverine $(H_2N-(CH_2)_5-NH_2)$ are produced from amino acids by the bacterial flora of the gut, in humans and animals.

CHAPTER 7

Biologically Important Compounds

All the biologically important compounds contain carbon, hydrogen and oxygen; some of them contain nitrogen, sulphur, iron and other elements as well. The main groups of compounds that are discussed in the present chapter are the carbohydrates, lipids, proteins, porphyrins, bile pigments, purines, pyrimidines, nucleic acids and high energy compounds.

Carbohydrates

The carbohydrates are a large family of compounds made up usually of carbon, hydrogen and oxygen, in the proportions: one carbon : two hydrogen : one oxygen (CH_2O). Carbohydrates make up a large part of plant and animal tissues, and serve as a most important source of energy for humans and animals. These compounds vary from simple molecules, generally called *sugars*, to very complex compounds known as *polysaccharides*. Sugars have a taste varying from tasteless to very sweet, depending on the compound concerned, and are generally white crystalline compounds. Their names generally end with the suffix *-ose*. The more complex carbohydrates are built up of long chains of sugar units joined together by the same type of linkage found in ethers, viz, R — O — R — O — R (see chapter 6).

Carbohydrates can be classified as follows:

1. *Monosaccharides* or simple sugars which can be subdivided according to the number of carbon atoms in their molecules, into the trioses ($C_3H_6O_3$), tetroses ($C_4H_8O_4$), pentoses ($C_5H_{10}O_5$) and hexoses ($C_6H_{12}O_6$). The way in which the various atoms are arranged in the molecules can also vary. Fig. 7.1 shows two trioses with different structures. The first one is known as glyceraldehyde since it has an aldehyde (CHO) group (Fig. 7.1a), and the second one is called dihydroxyacetone and contains a ketone (C=O) group (Fig. 7.1b). Each of the remaining carbon atoms in these molecules carry one hydroxyl (OH) group and the necessary hydrogen atoms to satisfy valency requirements. It can be stated as a general rule that sugars have either an aldehyde group, in which case they are called *aldoses* or a ketone group in which case they are referred to as *ketoses*.

Of the *trioses* the above-mentioned two, viz, glyceraldehyde and dihydroxyacetone are of special biochemical importance. They are formed as intermediary products in the metabolism of hexoses and pentoses in living cells. Tetroses are of little importance to us for the purposes of this discussion.

Pentoses (Fig. 7.1c-f) are very important in biological systems. Xylose and arabinose form part of complex carbohydrates found in plants. *Ribose* and *deoxyribose* are, however, the most important of this group of sugars. Ribose forms part of ribonucleic acid (RNA), while deoxyribose forms part of deoxyribonucleic acid (DNA), both of which are responsible for the intracellular control of metabolism and growth, as well as for the genetic regulation of cell function (see chapter 8). Ketopentoses, like xylulose and ribulose are intermediary products of pentose metabolism in cells.

Hexoses (Fig. 7.1g, h) like glucose, fructose, galactose and mannose are widely distributed in nature as part of various complex carbohydrates. Glucose and fructose occur free, as such, in the juices of a wide variety of fruits and vegetables. These sugars, and indeed the different pentoses and tetroses as well, differ from one another by virtue of differing internal arrangements of the atoms making up their molecules. Fructose and galactose are readily converted into glucose within the body.

Glucose (grape sugar or dextrose) is an aldohexose and is the immediate source of energy for the cells of the body. It is present in blood at a concentration that varies between 0,8 — 1,2g/l of blood and in this context it is generally referred to as the "blood sugar". *Blood sugar* represents glucose that is in transit from the alimentary canal to the liver, or from the liver to the extrahepatic tissues where most of it is used for the production of energy. The metabolism of glucose is discussed in Chapter 10 in detail.

The most important sources of glucose are fruit juices (e.g. grape juice) and vegetables, and it is present in honey together with fructose. It is also found in *glycosides*, in which it is combined with a great variety of non-carbohydrate compounds. Many glycosides, e.g. digitoxin, have important pharmacological properties.

Fructose (laevulose or fruit sugar) is the sweetest sugar known and is found in the juices of many ripe fruits and in honey. Fructose is also an intermediate product in the metabolism of glucose (see Fig. 10.3). It is an important source of energy for mammalian sperm cells, being present for this purpose in prostatic secretions.

2. *Disaccharides* ($C_{12}H_{22}O_{11}$) are made up of two hexoses joined together by an "ether" linkage. The most important of these compounds are sucrose (cane sugar), maltose (malt sugar) and lactose (milk sugar).

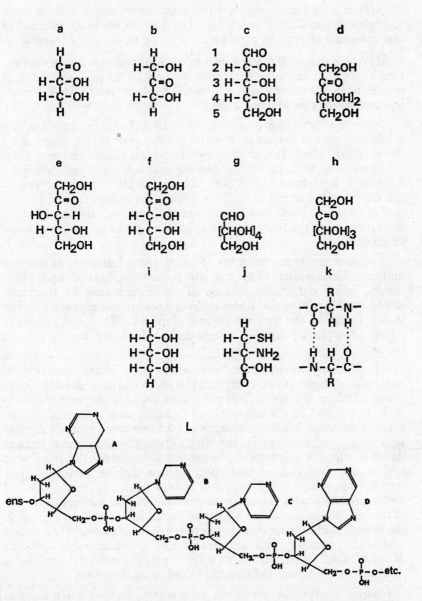

FIG. 7.1 Structure of organic compounds: (a) glyceraldehyde, (b) dihydroxyacetone, (c) an aldopentose, (d) a ketopentose, (e) xylulose, (f) ribulose, (g) an aldohexose, (h) a ketohexose, (i) glycerol, (j) cysteine, (k) hydrogen bonds in the spiral of protein molecules, (l) a tetranucleotide, part of DNA.

Sucrose is obtained mainly from sugar cane, sugar beet or from the juice of the Canadian maple. The sucrose molecule consists of one molecule of glucose combined with one molecule of fructose.

Maltose is one of the most important building sugar units occurring in complex carbohydrates such as the starches and glycogens. It is present in sprouting grain and in other plant tissues. Its molecule is made up of two glucose units.

Lactose is a sugar that is only found in milk, being produced by the mammary glands and as such is the main carbohydrate ingested by the suckling infant. It is slightly sweet and less soluble in water than sucrose and is built up of one glucose and one galactose molecule. Lactose is fermented by certain bacteria to lactic acid, for example during the souring of milk or during the production of cheeses and of yoghurt. Lactic acid can enter the same metabolic pathways as glucose (see Fig. 10.3a) and has therefore the same nutrient value as glucose.

3. *Polysaccharides* are built up of ten to some hundreds of pentose and/or hexose units. They are components of animal and plant tissues, being either constituents of cell membranes or represent stored carbohydrate, for instance liver and muscle glycogen or the starch found in the storage organs of plants. They are generally white, amorphous, tasteless compounds, which are poorly soluble in water.

3.1. *Homopolysaccharides* consist of long chains of only one type of sugar unit. They include compounds such as starches, dextrins, dextrans, cellulose, fructosans and pentosans. *Starch* is the reserve carbohydrate present in storage organs of plants, such as seeds, tubers, corms and roots. Maize, wheat, rice, potatoes and yams are important sources of starches in our diet. These starches, when broken down in the body, provide glucose for the tissues. We have seen earlier that two glucose molecules form a maltose molecule. The starches are composed of chains of maltose units, both unbranched and branched chains occurring in granules of native starch. The unbranched chains constitute a form of starch known as *amylose*, while the branched chains are usually referred to as *amylopectin*. When boiled with water, starch granules generally take up considerable amounts of water, swell, burst and form a thick gel, generally referred to as "starch paste", which is frequently used as an adhesive.

Dextrins are breakdown products of starch, formed when natural starch is treated with starch splitting enzymes or dilute acids. They are present in many plant tissues. Since their molecules are smaller than those of starches, they are regarded as being more digestible and are frequently used in the manufacture of "instant" beverages, baby foods, breakfast foods, malted milk preparations and so forth.

Dextrans are formed from glucose by the action of certain bacteria. They are often seen as slimes on decaying vegetables, notably on lettuce and carrots. Dextrans have no nutritional value, but are frequently used in solution as plasma substitutes for emergency transfusions.

Glycogens are animal starches, and represent the form in which glucose is stored in our bodies, specifically in the liver and muscles. Liver glycogen serves as the main source of the blood sugar, and our reserves of liver glycogen probably last for no longer than 6-12 hours after which they must be replenished either from dietary glucose or from glucose formed within the body from other compounds. Muscle glycogen is used entirely for muscle contraction and is replenished from the blood sugar.

Cellulose is the most abundant carbon-containing compound in nature. Its structure is similar to that of the starches, being built up out of units of a glucose containing disaccharide known as cellobiose. It is an undigestible compound but none-the-less is of considerable importance as the "roughage" in our diet. As such it lends bulk to the intestinal contents and stimulates peristaltic movements in the digestive tract. Cellulose-rich products such as bran, prunes and other dried fruits are often used for laxative purposes. Cellulose is almost exclusively of plant origin. Cotton and cotton-wool represent very pure forms of cellulose. Cellulose is used extensively in the manufacture of tissue-paper, toilet tissues, cellophane, photographic film and X-ray plates, rayon and explosives. Various cellulose derivatives, e.g. hydroxymethylcellulose possess the ability to absorb large volumes of water and to swell forming a gel, in much the same way as starches do. Since these compounds are indigestible, they are often used as bulkformers in various foods used for slimming purposes.

Fructosans are composed of long chains of fructose units and are found in the tubers of bulbs and the corms of certain plants such as dahlias, onions, garlic, chicory and artichokes, where they are present as reserve carbohydrates. The most important of these compounds is *inulin* which is used in studies of kidney function.

Fructosans cannot be digested and have no particular nutritional value. *Pentosans* are long chains of pentose units and are structural matter in many plants. These substances are also indigestible and contribute to the roughage in our diet. *Chitin* is a complex homopolysaccharide which forms the hard exoskeleton of insects, crabs, shrimps, prawns and crayfish.

3.2. *Heteropolysaccharides* are extremely complicated polysaccharides consisting of different sugars, derivatives of sugars and other substances. They are usually structural components of plant and animal tissues. Examples of this type of compound are gums and mucilages of plant origin, pectins, agar-agar, alginic acid, hyaluronic acid, chondroitin sulphate, heparin and the blood group substances.

Pectins are present in various fruits and vegetables, such as apples, quinces, citrus fruit and carrots. When these fruits or vegetables are boiled with the appropriate amount of sugar, they form clear edible gels, much used as jams, condiments and preserves. They have, however, little nutritive value.

Agar-agar is an indigestible carbohydrate extracted from various sea-weeds. It possesses the ability to absorb water, swell and form a firm gel which is much used as a medium for the culture of micro-organisms. Because of this property it is also used as a bulk-forming laxative.

Hyaluronic acid and *chondroitin sulphate* are components of various connective tissues in the body, whilst *heparin* is a natural anticoagulant, preventing the clotting of blood, within the vascular system. It is formed by the mast cells, large concentrations of which are present in the lungs and liver. It is often used as an anti-coagulant in the collection of blood samples. The *blood group substances* form part of the A-, B-, O- and Rh-antigens present in the red blood cells. These compounds are of great importance in blood transfusion.

Lipids

The lipids include fats, oils, waxes, fatty acids and various other compounds with fatlike properties. With a few exceptions these compounds are insoluble in water, but are usually soluble in solvents such as hot alcohol, chloroform, benzene, hexane and petroleum. As is the case with carbohydrates, fats perform a dual physiological function, viz, they are either structural components of cells or reserve stores of energy, and indeed represent the most important source of energy, their energy value being in the order of 37,8kJ/g. The equivalent value for carbohydrates and proteins is about 16kJ/g.

Lipids can be classified as follows:

1. *Fatty acids*. These have already been discussed under the carboxylic acids. Only those containing even numbers of carbon atoms in their chains are of physiological importance. Fatty acids with four to twelve carbon atoms are found in the fats of milk (in butter and cream). Fatty acids with sixteen to twenty carbon atoms are mainly found in animal tissues, and are the most important sources of stored energy. The most important of these acids are *palmitic acid, stearic acid* and *oleic acid*. Oleic acid is an unsaturated fatty acid.

2. *Glycerides* are lipids that contain glycerol as part of their molecules, and are in fact esters of glycerol. There are two main groups of these compounds, notably:

2.1. *Neutral fats* or *triglycerides*, the stored fat in the human or animal body. In fats of this type glycerol (Fig. 7.1i) is esterified with three fatty acid radicles, which may be the same acid radicle, or three different ones, e.g. in tripalmitin or oleopalmitostearin, respectively. Triglycerides that contain *unsaturated fatty acids*, such as oleic acid or linoleic acid, tend to be oils at room temperature and are mainly found in the seeds of plants. On the other hand triglycerides that contain *saturated fatty acids* such as stearic acid and palmitic acid, are generally solid fats at room temperature.

The fat stored in humans and animals is stored in characteristic sites, e.g. under the skin around the abdomen, on the buttocks, under the chin and behind the upper arm as well as around the heart, intestines and kidneys.

Soaps are the sodium and potassium salts of fatty acids and are obtained when neutral fats are boiled with dilute solutions of sodium or potassium hydroxide. This process is used in the manufacture of household soaps. Glycerol, released during the process, is an important by-product of the soap industry.

2.2. *Phospholipids* are structural components of animal and plant tissues. In the simplest form the glycerol is combined with two fatty acid radicles, with phosphoric acid and with nitrogenous bases such as choline ($HO \cdot CH_2 \cdot CH_2 \cdot N^+ (CH_3)_3$), ethanolamine ($HO \cdot CH_2 \cdot CH_2 \cdot NH_2$) or serine ($HO \cdot CH_2 \cdot CH \cdot COOH \cdot NH_2$). Phospholipids containing choline are known as *lecithins*, whilst those containing ethanolamine or serine are designated *cephalins*.

3. Lipids may be combined with non-liquid substances, e.g. proteins, as in the case of the *liproproteins* which are also components of cell membranes as well as being one of the forms in which lipids are transported in blood.

4. *Steroids* have already been mentioned under the tetracyclic hydrocarbons. The term is often loosely used to denote all derivatives of such hydrocarbons. The steroids of interest to us are all derivatives of *cholesterol* and include the *bile salts* (sodium taurocholate and sodium glycocholate), the *androgens* or male sex hormones (e.g. testosterone formed by certain cells of the testes), the *oestrogens* or *female sex hormones* (e.g. oestrone, oestradiol and oestriol formed by certain cells in the follicles of Graaf in the ovaries), *progesterone* (the hormone of the corpus luteum), the *glucocorticoids* (e.g. cortisol), the *mineralocorticoids* (e.g. aldosterone) and the precursors of vitamin D (e.g. 7-dehydrocholesterol).

Proteins

Proteins are the most important components of all living cells and contribute about 25% to the total body mass. Together with complex fats and polysaccharides, they form part of the structure of cells, but their most important function is as *enzymes* and *nucleoproteins*. Apart from these primary functions, proteins play a role in many other processes, serving for instance as reserve nutrients (see chapter 10), acting as buffers, and playing a role in the osmotic phenomena, which are so important in the regulation of the fluid compartments of the body.

The molecular mass of proteins ranges from a few thousand to many millions of daltons. They are composed of long chains of varying numbers of amino acids joined together in a specific sequence by peptide bonds. The number, sequence and type of amino acids present in the chains which make up the protein molecule, constitute the *primary structure* of proteins. These chains are invariably long and tend to adopt a helical form. The coils of the helices are generally held together by hydrogen bonds (Fig. 7.1k). In some instances adjacent chains may be linked by disulphide (S—S) bridges. Considerations of this nature are embraced by the term *secondary structure*. The term, the *tertiary structure* of proteins, denotes considerations such as the folding of helices to form globular, spherical or fibrous molecules.

Hydrogen bonds holding the coils of the helices together are readily broken by changes in the pH of the environment of the protein or by temperatures in excess of body temperature. Disruption of these bonds leads to alteration in the structure of the protein. If such changes are reversible, we speak of *denaturation* of the protein; if on the other hand they are irreversible, we speak of *coagulation*. Such changes are seen during the coagulation of milk, when acidic substances e.g. lemon juice (i.e. citric acid) are added to it, or the coagulation of egg albumen, when eggs are fried or boiled.

Proteins can be divided into the following groups:

1. *Fibrous proteins* which are insoluble, indigestible animal proteins found in silk, wool, hair, horns, nails, hoofs, connective tissues and bones.

Their tertiary structure takes the form of long parallel helices of peptide chains. Examples are *collagen*, the most important connective tissue protein, *elastin* found in tendons, walls of arteries and in other elastic tissue, and *keratins* in horn, wool, nails and hoofs. *Gelatin* is obtained from collagen during prolonged boiling in water.

2. *Globular proteins* which are water soluble molecules with a spherical tertiary structure. This group includes the enzymes, certain

hormones, the plasma proteins, tissue globulins and histones, and the protamines present in the nucleoproteins.

3. *Conjugated proteins* which contain a non-protein part of the molecule, often called a *prosthetic* group, and which is often responsible for the physiological functions of the protein molecule. The members of this group are the *nucleoproteins, mucoproteins, lipoproteins* and *chromoproteins*. The latter include the *haem chromoproteins* (e.g. haemoglobin and myoglobin, the cytochromes, etc.), and the *flavoproteins* (in which the prosthetic group is riboflavin or vitamin B_2).

Porphyrins and derivatives

The porphyrins form an interesting group of substances, which are widely distributed in nature, usually as part of complex molecules involved in *cellular respiration*. The ability to form porphyrins is a very primitive attribute possessed by all forms of life. Apart from their respiratory function, porphyrins also form part of various pigments present in hair, feathers and egg shells of animals and birds.

In a previous chapter we encountered the compound, porphin, with its macrocyclic type of structure (Fig. 6.41). This compound, although entirely synthetic in origin, is considered to be the hypothetical parent substance of a large variety of derivatives, the porphyrins. They differ from one another by the various groups which substitute for the hydrogen atoms on the porphin structure as well as by the number and position of double bonds within the macrocyclic structure itself.

The most important porphyrins which occur in human and animal tissues are the *uroporphyrins* (containing eight carboxyl groups), the *coproporphyrins* (containing four carboxyl groups) and the *protoporphyrins* (carrying two carboxyl groups). Small amounts of various porphyrins normally occur in the stools. A dramatic increase in the faecal and urinary output of these compounds occurs in the group of related diseases collectively known as *the porphyrias*.

Porphyrins possess the ability to combine with metallic elements such as magnesium, iron and copper. The resulting derivatives, known as metalloporphyrins, often form the prosthetic group present in various chromoproteins. *Haem*, an iron-containing protoporphyrin, is for instance the functional part of the molecules of the respiratory pigments, *haemoglobin, myoglobin* and the *cytochromes* as well as being part of the hydrogen peroxide (H_2O_2)-splitting enzymes, catalase and peroxidase. The green respiratory pigment of plants, chlorophyll, is a magnesium containing porphyrin.

Purines, Pyrimidines and their derivatives

These very important compounds form part of the molecules of the nucleic acids, DNA and RNA, of high energy compounds such as ATP and of co-enzymes like NAD, NADP and FAD (see following chapter).

Purines characteristically contain the purine ring-system of atoms depicted in Fig. 6.4j, in which one or more of the substituent hydrogen atoms are replaced by amino, oxygen, or hydroxyl-groups. Depending on the nature and the extent of this replacement, different purines can be formed and the most important for our purposes are the compounds *adenine, guanine, hypoxanthine, xanthine* and *uric acid.* The first two occur in the nucleic acids, DNA and RNA; adenine occurs in the co-enzymes mentioned, while the latter three purines result from the metabolic transformation of adenine and guanine in the body. Uric acid is generally regarded as representing the end point of purine metabolism in the human body and is apparently entirely a waste product, which is excreted via the urine.

The molecules of the *pyrimidines* are somewhat similar in structure to those of the purines, but containing the pyrimidine ring system depicted in Fig. 6.4k. Once more depending on the nature and extent of substitution of the hydrogen atoms, various pyrimidines are possible, the most important ones for living cells being *uracil, thymine* and *cytosine.* Since both the purines and pyrimidines have alkaline properties they are often referred to as *nitrogenous bases,* or simply *bases,* in discussions on their physiological functions (see below).

Nucleosides are compounds containing a purine or a pyrimidine, combined with either ribose or deoxyribose. *Adenosine* is adenine combined with ribose; *cytidine* is cytosine combined with ribose, and the guanine- and uracil-containing nucleotides are named *guanosine* and *uridine* respectively.

Nucleotides are simply nucleosides containing an orthophosphoric acid group attached to the sugar. They are, in other words, *nucleoside monophosphates,* and are either named as such, e.g. *adenosine monophosphate* (AMP), guanosine monophosphate (GMP), uridine monophosphate (UMP), etc.; or since this phosphoric acid group confers upon their molecules strongly acidic properties, they may be named accordingly, *adenylic acid* (AMP), *guanylic acid* (GMP), *thymidylic acid* (*thymidine monophosphate,* TMP), *cytidylic acid* (*cytidinine monophosphate,* CMP) and *uridylic acid* (UMP).

It is in the form of nucleotides that the purine and pyrimidine bases are generally present in the nucleic acids, DNA and RNA. We have seen, however, that adenine is also present in the co-enzymes NAD, NADP, and FAD. These compounds have a dinucleotide type of structure, i.e. two nucleotides joined together, but are remarkable in that the second nucleotide unit contains nicotinic acid (vitamin B_3) in the case of NAD and NADP, pantothenic acid in the case of co-enzyme A, or riboflavin (vitamin B_2) in the case of FAD. In vitamin B_{12}, this type of structure is further complicated by the presence of a cobalt atom.

Further phosphate groups can be attached to the one already present in compounds like AMP, CMP or UMP, giving rise to adenosine diphosphate (ADP), *adenosine triphosphate* (ATP), cytidine di- and triphosphate (CDP and CTP respectively) and uridine di- and triphosphate (UDP and UTP respectively). These compounds are often collectively referred to as *nucleotide phosphates*. Their role in metabolic processes will be discussed later.

Nucleic Acids

These compounds are fundamental to life. There are two types of nucleic acids present in cells, notably deoxyribonucleic acid (DNA) and ribonucleic acid (RNA). The former, *DNA*, is largely found within the nuclei of cells and is a repository of *genetic information* relating to the differentiation, growth and function of tissues. *RNA* on the other hand occurs in various forms which are associated with *protein synthesis* and the transfer across the cell of genetic information relating to this phenomenon. A detailed explanation of these processes is given in the next chapter.

The molecules of *deoxyribonucleic acid* (DNA) consist of a long chain of nucleotides folded in the form of a double helix (Fig. 7.2). The nucleotides which are present in large numbers in the chain are adenylic acid, guanylic acid, cytidylic acid and thymidylic acid, abbreviated in the discussions which follow to A, G, C and T respectively. Uridylic acid (U) does not occur in DNA but makes up part of the RNA molecule (from which thymidylic acid is generally absent).

The sugar present in these nucleotides is, as the name DNA implies, deoxyribose. The backbone of the molecule is made up of deoxyribose units joined by the phosphate groups belonging to each nucleotide unit (Fig. 7.2). The purine and pyrimidine bases protrude from the sides of the DNA strand. The two strands of the double helix of the DNA molecule are held together by hydrogen bonding between these bases (Fig. 7.2), There is a remarkable feature about this, however, and one of which we must take particular note. The bases lying opposite one another in the double helix and between which the holding hydrogen bonds are formed, occur in the form of *complementary* pairs. *Adenine always lies opposite to, and binds with thymine; cytosine always lies opposite to, and binds with, guanine.* Each com-

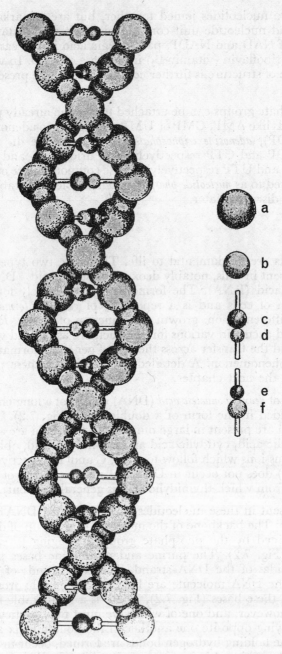

Fig. 7.2   The double helix of the DNA molecule: (a) deoxyribose, (b) phosphoric acid, (c) adenine, (d) thymine, (e) cytosine, (f) guanine.

plementary pair thus consists of a purine (adenine *or* guanine), and a pyrimidine (cytidine *or* thymidine). Study Fig. 7.2 once more and note anew the pairs

$$—A \longleftrightarrow T—$$
$$—C \longleftrightarrow G—$$

extending across and holding the coils of the helices together. We shall be referring frequently to these *complementary pairs* of bases and it is essential that at this stage the reader has clarity in his mind on this point. Note that each full turn of the helix contains ten pairs of nucleotides.

The DNA molecules are located in the chromosomes present in the nuclei of our tissue cells. Human chromosomes contain about 15% DNA, 10% RNA and 75% of protein. The molecules of both DNA and RNA are associated with varying amounts of proteins, to form *nucleoproteins*. This is particularly true for DNA. The molecular masses of the large aggregates of DNA within the chromosomes may approach millions.

The molecules of *ribonucleic acid* (RNA), consist of a single long strand of nucleotides. These nucleotides contain only four of the previously mentioned bases, namely, adenine, guanine, cytosine and uracil. Thymine is only present in one particular type of RNA, namely transfer-RNA (t-RNA) (see below), which is therefore exceptional in this respect. The sugar present in these nucleotides is, as the name implies, ribose. As in the case of DNA, the nucleotides in RNA are held together by the phosphate groups, which link the ribose units in each nucleotide to form the backbone of the molecule. In the single stranded RNA molecules, the purine and pyrimidine bases consequently project from the "sides" of the molecule. This arrangement is as we shall see in the following chapter, of considerable importance in the transfer of genetic information during protein synthesis, and in the process of protein synthesis itself.

Some different types of RNA molecules occur within cells, each of which fulfils a different function, namely:

1. *Messenger-RNA* (m-RNA) carries genetic information from the DNA molecules present in the nucleus to the ribosomes present in the cytoplasm of cells.

2. *Ribosomal RNA* (r-RNA), which is present in the ribosomes of cells. Although its exact function is by no means clear at the moment, it apparently serves as a support upon which protein molecules can be synthesized.

3. *Transfer RNA* (t-RNA) is exceptional as far as RNA in general is concerned, in that the base thymine is present in its constituent nucleotides in addition to adenine, guanine, cytosine and uracil. This

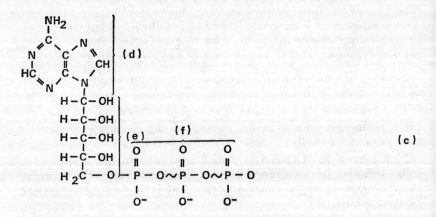

FIG. 7.3   (a) Pyrophosphoric acid, (b) pyrophosphate ion, (c) ATP, (d) adenine, (e) ribose, and (f) triphosphate.

permits the formation of helices, much like those present in the DNA molecule and also ensures that all the members of the complementary base pairs are present somewhere in the t-RNA molecule. The short t-RNA molecules serve as carriers of amino acids during protein synthesis, carrying these from the cytoplasm to the ribosomes.

Viruses contain varying amounts of nucleic acids. These also vary in composition and structure from virus to virus. Viruses are organisms which cause disease in plants, animals and man. Those affecting plants contain only DNA, while those affecting man and animals may be similar in composition, or may contain both DNA and RNA. Since no living cell can exist without both types of nucleic acid being present, viruses which contain only DNA, or only RNA, can only exist as parasites in living cells, where they make use of the host's RNA or DNA, as the case may be, to assist them in their replication and continued existence. It is for this reason that vaccines for use against viruses can only be prepared by using living culture media, either laboratory animals, cell cultures or living chick embryos.

Compounds containing high energy phosphate bonds

Mention has already been made of the fact that when chemical bonds form between atoms, a certain amount of energy becomes inherent in the bond in order to hold the atoms making up the particular molecule together. When these bonds are broken, this energy is liberated into the system in which the reaction is taking place. During the discussions on metabolism which follow in the succeeding chapters, we shall meet compounds such as glucose-6-phosphate and fructose-6-phosphate. Since glucose and fructose are alcohols, the compounds just mentioned are their phosphate esters, formed by them combining with orthophosphoric acid with the elimination of water, according to the general equation

$$A \cdot H + B \cdot OH \rightleftarrows A \cdot B + H_2O$$
$$\text{acid} \quad \text{alcohol} \quad \text{ester} \quad \text{water}$$

The bonds which unite the parent alcohol and orthophosphoric acid in these compounds are the familiar covalent bonds. When bonds in esters of this type are broken, the amount of energy set free is in the order of 9 200 — 14 600 joule per mole (gram molecular mass).

We have on numerous occasions so far made mention of the fact that a considerable amount of energy can be stored in the compound adenosine triphosphate (ATP). This compound is a nucleotide phosphate and its structure is shown in Fig. 7.3. It will be seen that one phosphate group is directly attached to the ribose portion of the molecule, whereas the remaining two are attached to this one and to one another. The three chemical bonds concerned are once more our familiar covalent bonds. When the one between ribose and its phosphate group is broken, the energy yield is approximately 9 200 joule per mole of ATP. This bond is an ester bond similar to that present in the phosphate esters mentioned above. When the two terminal phosphate bonds of the ATP molecule are broken, the energy yield is approximately 30 500 joule/mole of ATP for each one of them; a significantly higher yield than in the first instance. The total amount of energy which could be obtained from ATP if all three phosphate bonds were broken simultaneously is approximately 70 200 joule per mole. Now this is considerably higher than the amount liberated when a compound like glucose-6-phosphate is split. For this reason nucleotide phosphates like ATP are frequently referred to as *"high energy phosphates"* and the two terminal phosphate bonds are frequently referred to as *"high energy phosphate bonds"*, in contradistinction to the "low energy phosphate bond" in a compound like glycerol phosphate. These "high energy phosphate bonds" are generally designated by the symbol $\sim$ (P), the wavy line indicating their apparently different nature (Fig. 7.3).

It has just been said that all three of the bonds attaching the phosphate groups to the ribose in the ATP molecule are our familiar covalent bonds. How then are we to explain the considerably higher energy yield from the two terminal bonds? In order to do so, we must digress for a moment and study the formation of the compound, pyrophosphoric acid (Fig. 7.3). When ordinary orthophosphoric acid is heated for a fairly long time at 250°-260°C, its molecules pair up to form pyrophosphoric acid according to the equation

$$2H_3PO_4 = H_4P_2O_7 + H_2O$$

The two phosphate radicals ($H_2PO_3^-$) in this structure are joined to the central oxygen atom by covalent bonds. There is apparently nothing unusual about the group of atoms — P — O — P — (or (P) — O — (P)), which is referred to as the *pyrophosphate* group or *pyrophosphate* bond. The name pyrophosphate is derived from the classical Greek word for fire, namely *pur*, indicating the source of the energy needed to form these bonds.

A glance at the structure of ATP (Fig. 7.3) will show that the two terminal phosphate groups are in fact present as pyrophosphate groups. Salts of pyrophosphoric acid, such as sodium pyrophosphate, are reasonably stable substances under the usual laboratory conditions, yet ATP is a labile substance in the sense that the two terminal phosphate bonds are readily broken in living cells with the liberation of the large amount of energy mentioned. The reason for this lies in the fact that at the pH of tissue fluids the pyrophosphate groups of ATP are ionized as shown in Fig. 7.3. Three strongly negative charged groups are thus adjacent to one another. Now we know that it is an elementary rule, that like charges repel each other, and the repelling forces exerted by the three phosphate groups on one another are considerable. In order to hold the ATP molecule together, sufficient intramolecular energy must be present to overcome these repelling forces and so hold the phosphate groups together. The *additional* energy is thus inherent in the molecule as a whole, rather than in the covalent bonds between the phosphate groups.

A number of nucleotide phosphates of the ATP type are of considerable importance in living cells, for instance *uridine triphosphate* (UTP), *guanosine triphosphate* (GTP) and *cytidine triphosphate* (CTP). It must be mentioned at this stage that compounds of this type are not the only ones in which high energy phosphate bonds occur, nor are such bonds necessarily in the form of pyrophosphate groups. Of importance are, for instance, *carboxyl-phosphate* groups as in the compound diphosphoglyceric acid, enol-phosphate groups as in phosphoenolpyruvic acid, and guanidine-phosphate groups as in creatine phosphate, which yield 49 300, 61 800 and 43 000 joule/mol respectively, when the "high energy" phosphate bond concerned is broken. We will meet these compounds again during the discussions on metabolism in the chapters which follow.

Mention has been made of the fact that in order to make pyrophosphoric acid in the laboratory, orthophosphoric acid has to be heated for a relatively long while at 250°-260°C, yet in the body our tissue cells manufacture ATP with ease and at a bewilderingly fast rate. How is this achieved? We have already taken note of the fact that most of the reactions taking place in living cells are promoted by the action of enzymes. The synthesis (and breakdown) of ATP is mediated by enzymes known as *adenosine triphosphatases* (ATP-ases) in reactions such as the following:

$$\text{ATP} \underset{\text{ATP-ase}}{\rightleftharpoons} \text{ADP} + \text{Pi} + 30\ 500\ \text{joule/mole.}$$

$$\text{ADP} \underset{\text{ATP-ase}}{\rightleftharpoons} \text{AMP} + \text{Pi} + 30\ 500\ \text{joule/mole.}$$

The symbol Pi is used to designate the phosphate ion, in contradistinction to $-\text{\textcircled{P}}$ which indicates a phosphate group. At the pH of body tissues, the symbol Pi indicates the two phosphate ions $HPO_4^=$ and $H_2PO_4^-$ which are present in tissue fluids in the ratio of 4:1.

In a few metabolic reactions ATP is broken down as follows:

$$\text{ATP} \underset{\text{ATP-ase}}{\rightleftharpoons} \text{AMP} + \text{PPi} + 30\ 500\ \text{joule/mole.}$$

The symbol PPi denotes the pyrophosphate ion. As fast as it forms it is generally degraded by the enzyme *pyrophosphatase* to yield phosphate ions and energy.

CHAPTER 8

Enzymatic and Genetic Control of Reactions

The chemical reactions which take place in living systems proceed at an amazingly *fast rate* when compared to the rate at which the same reactions would take place in a test tube under experimental conditions. The acceleration of these reactions in biological systems is achieved by *enzymes*. Enzymes are *catalysts*, i.e., they can accelerate a reaction without themselves being permanently altered during the process. As a result of their catalyzing ability enzymes have two very important functions.

1. *Enzymes localize reactions.* A chemical reaction will generally proceed on its own anywhere at its own slow rate provided that the reactants are freely available and that other essential conditions are met. The same reaction will, however, proceed at a faster and therefore more useful rate, in those parts of the body, or those particular cells or tissues where it is actually required for physiological purposes and where the catalyzing enzyme is actually present. The presence of large amounts of an enzyme in a certain tissue determines therefore to a large extent, where a particular type of reaction will take place in the body. This localization of function is even more evident within cells, where certain types of reactions are confined to the mitochondria, others to the cell sap and yet others to the nucleus and so on.

2. *Enzymes determine the rate of reactions.* The extent to which reactions are accelerated depends on the amount of enzymes that will have to combine, even though temporarily, with the reactants or *substrates* as they are called in this case.

Since each type of chemical reaction in the tissues of the body is determined by the localization and availability of enzymes, the total arrangements of chemical reactions in the body to form an integrated biochemical whole will be determined by these factors as well. We know that all enzymes are proteins and as such are produced under the genetic supervision of the DNA in cell nuclei. We can therefore safely say that the organisation of all the chemical reactions in the body of an individual is determined by the *genetic* information that has been passed on through DNA from his or her parents, as the case may be.

The enzymatic activity of any given tissue depends not only on organizational factors but also on the general physiological activity of the individual at any given time. Think for instance of periodic work or exercise and the corresponding increase of enzymic activity which must occur to permit this. Quite apart from such voluntary phenomena and considerations like the speeding up of movement and secretions in the digestive tract following a meal, quite a few enzymically mediated processes in the body show a rhythmic periodicity of increased activity, governing to a very large extent behavioural patterns in many animals. Such variations of enzymic activity with time, or circadian rhythms as they are called, are controlled largely by *local tissue factors* and *neurohormonal mechanisms*. Local tissue factors, such as the accumulation of the products of metabolism, which determine amongst other things, the rate of flow of blood through muscle tissues, are of direct interest to us.

Enzyme action and substrate specificity

The most important proteins in the body are the enzymes. We may compare the action of an enzyme to that of a person introducing two of his or her friends that were hitherto unknown to one another and who by nature of their mutual interests could become close friends. The person doing the introductions can leave the scene of the introductions without himself undergoing any such emotional change. The molecules on which the enzymes perform their action are known as *substrates*. These would correspond to the persons being introduced in our analogy above; the enzyme being the introducer. An important property of enzymes is that they can only act on specific substrates and once again we can only introduce people to others if we have some specific knowledge of them. Thus specific knowledge implies a certain type of relationship which we shall endeavour to illustrate below. In terms of enzyme action we talk of the substrate specificity of enzymes. Let us look at a model of enzyme action (Fig. 8.1) in which the substrate (*a*) must be split into two parts. The enzyme (*b*) binds with the substrate (*a*) to form an unstable intermediate product (*c*). The manner is which this happens is similar to the manner in which the parts of a jig-saw puzzle are put together. The structure of the enzyme is such that it can only fit on to certain well-defined structures on the particular substrate and therefore it can only bind with this substrate and no other one which does not possess the required binding sites. This is the reason for the specificity. When the substrate comes into contact with the enzyme the required reaction can take place. Since the intermediate product is unstable it breaks up spontaneously yielding the free enzyme (*d*) and the products (*e*), of the reaction. The enzyme is unchanged and can be used again. If the reaction is reversible it can proceed until equilibrium is reached. This aspect will be discussed later, but at this stage we can simply note that reaching equilibrium means that the rate of splitting of the substrate (*a*) is equal to the rate of recombination of the products (*e*), the enzyme catalyzing the reaction in either direction depending on circumstances which will become clearer later.

As a further illustration of the substrate specificity of enzymes we can consider the models shown in Fig 8.2. The enzyme depicted here is succinic dehydrogenase and its natural substrate is succinic acid as shown in Fig. 8.2(a). Binding between the substrate and the enzyme is shown as occurring here through the medium of ionized carboxyl groups

$$(C-O^-)$$
$$\|$$
$$O$$

and corresponding positive charges on the surface of the enzyme. The size of the substrate molecule is such that it "fits" the binding sites on the surface of the enzyme. In Fig. 8.2(b) and 8.2(c) is shown what would occur if the enzyme was brought into contact with molecules different from but closely related to succinic acid. In these cases the chain lengths are such that binding can only occur at one of the two sites shown on the enzyme surface, and since the binding is imperfect no reaction can occur. The enzyme, succinic dehydrogenase is thus specific for succinic acid.

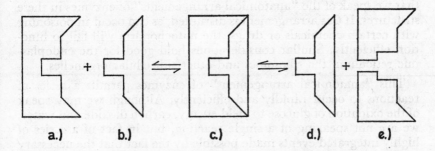

a.)   b.)   c.)   d.)   e.)

Fig. 8.1   A model of enzyme action. (a) substrate, (b) enzyme, (c) intermediate product, (d) enzyme, and (e) the final products of the reaction.

Localization of enzymes in tissues

Reference was made in the opening paragraphs of this chapter to the localization of enzymes in tissues. Some amplification of these earlier thoughts is necessary at this stage. During the embryonic life of the individual differentiation of his body tissues occurs; that is they commence to take on their characteristic form and in many instances start to assume their characteristic physiological functions. At this stage high concentrations of enzymes characteristic of a particular tissue start to form in the organs concerned and this particular growth of metabolic machinery continues through foetal life into the neonatal period. We find for instance that at birth, many of the enzymes required for digestion are being secreted by the appropriate parts of the gastro-intestinal tract, for instance salivary amylase, pepsin in the gastric juice and trypsin in the pancreatic juice. As the individual grows through neonatal life, so the production of these enzymes and hence digestion as a whole becomes more efficient. By the same token, enzymes found in characteristically high concentrations in liver, muscle, nervous tissue and other tissues are produced in increasing amounts as the tissues concerned become functional. In order to integrate biochemical events into the smoothly functioning harmonious whole which we call the living and healthy individual, these events have to be minutely organized right down to the subcellular level. So it is then, that different parts of the cells of any particular tissue, perform different but highly integrated functions. The nucleus, which is a repository of genetic information, directs metabolic activity throughout the cell, the mitochondria produce energy and ATP and the cell membranes control the to-and-fro flow of nutrient and waste materials.

The enzymes that carry out all these precise functions are therefore located exactly in the cell where they are to function. In the mitochondria this localization of enzymes is for instance so precise that we speak of the "anatomical arrangements" of enzymes in these structures. If this arrangement is disrupted, as can occur in poisoning with certain chemicals or drugs, the mitochondria will fail to function efficiently. Similar considerations hold good for the endoplasmic reticulum, the ribosomes and other subcellular organelles.

This "anatomical arrangement" of enzymes permits a series of reactions to occur rapidly and efficiently. Although we may speak of the oxidation of glucose to yield energy, carbon dioxide and water, we are not speaking of a single reaction, but in fact of a series of highly integrated events made possible by the fact that the necessary enzymes are located intracellularly in very close proximity to one another. As the products of one of the reactions in the series form, so the necessary enzymes are there to take the process further until the glucose is finally and usefully degraded into simple products like carbon dioxide and water; with the simultaneous release of the energy inherent in the chemical bonds making up the glucose molecule, as heat.

As we proceed in our study of metabolic processes within the body, so the importance of the localization or compartmentalization of enzymes within cells and tissues, will become clearer.

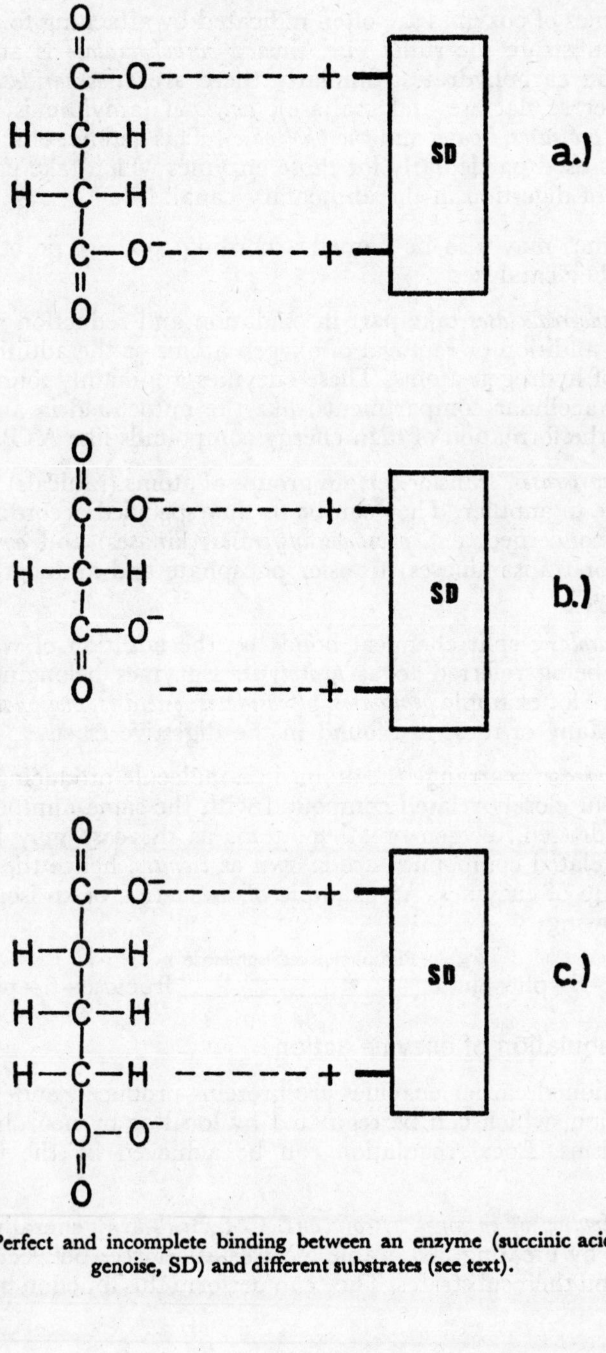

Fıg. 8.2 Perfect and incomplete binding between an enzyme (succinic acid dehydrogenoise, SD) and different substrates (see text).

The types of enzymes found in tissues

The names of enzymes are often indicated by attaching to the name of the substrate the suffix *-ase*, thus a *carbohydratase* is an enzyme acting on carbohydrates. Similarly there are *disaccharidases* (including sucrase, lactase and maltase), *amylases* (amylum is Latin for starch), *proteases*, *lipases* and *phospholipases*. This manner of naming enzymes is used particularly for those enzymes which take part in the process of digestion in the alimentary canal.

Enzymes may also be named according to the type of reaction which they catalyze:

A.   *Oxido-reductases* take part in oxidation and reduction reactions, i.e., the addition or removal of oxygen atoms or the addition or removal of hydrogen atoms. These enzymes are mainly found in certain intracellular compartments, like the mitochondria and play a part in the formation of high energy compounds like ATP.

B.   *Transferases*, transfer certain groups of atoms (radicals) from one substrate to another. They can be further specified according to the radical concerned, e.g. *phosphotransferases* (kinases) and *amino transferases* (or transaminases) transfer phosphate and aminogroups respectively.

C.   *Hydrolases* split chemical bonds by the addition of water; the process being referred to as *hydrolysis*. Enzymes belonging to this group are for example *peptidases*, *glycosidases*, *esterases*, *phosphatases*, and so on. Many of these are found in the digestive tract.

D.   *Isomerases* rearrange the atoms in a molecule producing thereby a new but closely related compound with the same number of carbon, hydrogen, oxygen or other atoms as the case may be. Such closely related compounds are known as *isomers*, hence the name of this group of enzymes. An example of the action of an isomerase is the following:

$$\text{Glucose}-6-\text{phosphate} \xrightleftharpoons{\text{Phosphohexose isomerase}} \text{fructose}-6-\text{phosphate}$$

Local regulation of enzyme action

As mentioned earlier enzymes are proteins produced under genetic supervision, which can be regulated by local or by neurohormonal mechanisms. Local regulation can be achieved by the following means:

A.   *Activation of enzymes by cofactors*. Cofactors are generally cations that act by creating favourable electrostatic forces between the enzymes and their substrates. They can perform this function by adding new electrostatic forces or by removing forces that might hinder the formation of bonds. The most important cofactors are bivalent cations (e.g. calcium, Ca^{++}, magnesium, Mg^{++} and manganese, Mn^{++}) as well as some monovalent cations (e.g. K^+).

B. *The creation of optimum conditions for enzyme action*

1. *Optimum temperature.* It was mentioned in chapter 1 that chemical reactions will only take place if the subunits of the reacting substances possess kinetic energy, i.e. if they move. The greater the rate of movement the more are the chances for reaction between the subunits and the faster will the reaction proceed. This of course is also true for enzyme action which becomes more efficient with increased temperature. This only holds true within physiological limits, since as enzymes are proteins, they become damaged through denaturation at high temperatures (see chapter 7). It is probable that many of the manifestations of a high *fever* result from damage to certain enzyme systems.

At temperatures lower than that of the body the rate of enzyme ac'ion will also be slowed down, but in this instance no damage occurs to the enzyme molecule. The rate of movement of the substrate molecules is simply decreased, hence the chances of reacting with the enzyme are lessened.

Use is made of this fact when operations are performed under *hypothermia*. The patient is cooled down to about 30°C during the operation. The resulting low metabolic rate brings about low respiratory, circulation and excretory rates, thus lessening many of the risks attending deep anaesthesia and major surgery.

2. *Optimum pH.* Enzymes act best at a *specific* pH, which lies within a narrow range of hydrogen ion concentrations. For most enzymes in the tissues of the body the pH at which they will act best is in the region of 7,2 to 7,4 which is of course normal tissue pH. The enzymes of the digestive tract show other optimal pH ranges. For example, salivary amilase requires an optimum pH of 6,0-7,0 gastric juice pepsin, a pH of 1,5-2,5 and trypsin in the pancreatic juice a pH of about 8,0. If the pH is not optimal the action of the enzyme will be inhibited. For example, when we eat bread which consists to a large extent of starches, digestion starts in the mouth when the salivary amylase is mixed with the bread during chewing. The pH in this case is 7,2-7,4; therefore favourable. When the bread mixed with amylase reaches the stomach, digestion is immediately inhibited on the surface of the food mass by the low pH of gastric juice. Inside the food mass starch digestion by amylase proceeds until the pH of the whole mass is significantly lowered by the penetration of the gastric juices.

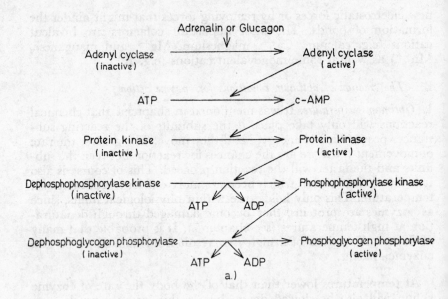

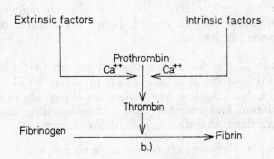

FIG. 8.3   Examples of cascade mechanisms.

C.   Activation of proenzymes. In many instances an enzyme is produced by the cells concerned in an inactive form known as a *proenzyme*. This is the case with a number of the powerful proteolytic enzymes, e.g. pepsin and trypsin, which are produced by certain cells in the stomach and the pancreas in the inactive forms, pepsinogen and trypsinogen respectively. Had this not been so, these enzymes would act upon proteinaceous structures in the cells producing them. Once the gastric juice has reached the stomach cavity, pepsinogen is activated by hydrochloric acid, which is also present in gastric juice and protein digestion can then proceed. The mucous membrane lining the stomach is protected from the proteolytic effects of pepsin by a continuous production of mucus. If for any reason this protective mechanism breaks down, pepsin may damage the mucous membranes of the stomach with the resultant formation of peptic ulcers.

The activation of proenzymes is in some cases brought about by other enzymes and it can result in a series of proenzyme-enzyme conversions (*cascade mechanisms*). A number of instances are now known where more complex processes are mediated by a series of enzymes, which sequentially activate one another until the final effect is achieved. This final effect is often the initiation of an involved but vital physiological process. For example the enzyme *enterokinase* activates *trypsinogen* in the pancreatic juice to *trypsin*. Trypsin further activates *chymotrypsinogen* to *chymotrypsin*. Both trypsin and *chymotrypsin* are proteolytic enzymes that act in the small intestine, the mucous membrane of which is also shielded from their proteolytic activity by mucous secretions.

The cascade of events may also be triggered off by substances or enzymes liberated from injured cells as seen in the *coagulation of blood* or in the *liberation of pain-producing substances* (kinins) or it may be triggered off by the action of a hormone on a particular tissue, as in the case of *glycogenolysis*.

The process of activation of the latter system is often used as a model to explain the action of hormones at the cellular level and it is perhaps fitting that we should pause for a moment and examine it in some detail (Fig. 8.3). In very general terms we can say that the hormones, *adrenalin* and *glucagon* act upon liver and muscle tissue stimulating the breakdown of stored glycogen with the resulting formation of glucose for use in the production of energy. In more specific terms these hormones can be said to stimulate the action of the enzyme *glycogen phosphorylase*, one of the enzymes involved in the initial hydrolysis of the glycogen molecule. Exactly how do these hormones achieve this? All the details are not yet known with certainty but the process of activation proceeds along the following lines. It is assumed in the first instance that binding sites, to which these hormones can attach themselves, are present on the membranes of liver and muscle cells. This attachment is assumed to occur in much the same way as envisaged in our earlier discussion on the binding of enzymes with their substrates. This means that hormones can only act on those tissues where specific binding sites for them exists — a phenomenon which helps to explain the specific action of many hormones. These binding sites are often referred to as *receptors*, a term borrowed from pharmacology and not to be confused with the receptors of nervous tissue.

It is assumed now that the combination of hormone and membrane receptor activates the enzyme *adenyl cyclase*, located somewhere in its immediate vicinity. Adenyl cyclase in turn acts upon the well-known compound ATP converting it into *cyclic adenosine monophosphate* (*cyclic-AMP* or *c-AMP*). This cyclic AMP is known to activate many metabolic processes, amongst which is the activation of the enzyme *phosphorylase kinase*. This enzyme in its turn brings about the activation of glycogen phosphorylase and the process of glycogenolysis commences.

The whole process can be likened to the unlocking of many doors, one after the other. At first glance the mechanism may seem involved and devious and we may quite rightly ask why this should be. No simple pat answer can be forthcoming. Nevertheless we can endeavour to do so by bearing in mind some important points already mentioned elsewhere in the text. Metabolism is in general a highly integrated series of biochemical events. To permit this integration a high degree of specificity of enzymes or hormone action is required; timing delays, however infinitesimally small they may be, are necessary and the insertion of numerous safety devices are required to ensure that events follow a smooth course. Considerations like specificity, delays in timing and safety factors are all inherent in a cascade mechanism. In mechanisms of this type one of the enzymes at the beginning of the cascade often fulfills the role of a master-key. If it is activated the others are activated in turn automatically. We will refer to enzymes playing such a role as "key-enzymes" in our subsequent discussions of metabolism.

D.   *Regulation of the substrates and products of the reaction.* Reversible reactions have already been discussed (chapter 4). We have noted that when the ratio of the concentrations of the reacting substances on either side of the equation reach a certain value, the reaction ceases. The only way in which the reaction can proceed further is by the addition of more substrate or by removal of the products of the reaction. The removal of products from the tissue cells takes place by diffusion or active transport to the blood and thence to the organs of excretion. In many cases, however, the product of a particular reaction must be used in further reactions and hence the transport of such products must take place in a very organised way. Various *co-enzymes* are used in many instances to perform this transfer function. By the same token additional substrates are being continually transported to areas of very active metabolism like the liver, heart muscle and skeletal muscle, from various storage depots in the body, and from the alimentary canal, by the blood.

The action of a co-enzyme can be illustrated by means of a simple example. Substrate A in the equation below is broken down by a certain enzyme to form the product B and two hydrogen ions, viz,

$$A \xrightleftharpoons{\text{enzyme}} B + 2H^+$$

The presence of free hydrogen ions in tissue fluids presents a great problem, since they can change the pH of tissue fluid appreciably and thereby influence all other reactions taking place in the cell concerned. These embarrassing hydrogen ions can be removed by the intervention of the compound known as *nicotine-adenine-dinucleotide* (*NAD*), with the formation of reduced NAD (NADH$_2$)

$$A + NAD \overset{\text{enzyme}}{\rightleftharpoons} B + NADH_2$$

The compound NAD has acted here as a co-enzyme to the enzyme indicated in our example, by effectively removing the hydrogen ions from the vicinity of the main enzyme reaction (see also chapter 10). Since the reaction is indicated as being a reversible one NADH$_2$ can supply hydrogen ions for the reverse reaction, thereby reverting to its former state (NAD). Hence in this instance the co-enzyme either removes hydrogen atoms from, or supplies them to, the main enzyme-catalyzed reaction, depending upon the direction this takes. Since the hydrogen ions are merely shuttled back and forth between substrate and co-enzyme, the hydrogen ion concentration of the cell-sap is not influenced in any way. Other co-enzymes, such as FAD, co-enzyme Q, cytochromes and co-enzyme A will be encountered in later chapters.

Coding of genetic information

One of the most important ways in which the direction and rate of metabolic reactions can be controlled is by exerting this control on the synthesis of the enzymes which are required to carry out the reactions concerned. Since, as far as we know, all enzymes are proteins, this control devolves upon the process of protein synthesis. The ability of DNA to control protein synthesis lies in the "genetic code" inherent in the structure of DNA.

Look carefully now at the schematic representation of part of the double helix of the DNA molecule presented in Fig. 8.4. The pairs of complementary bases holding the two strands of DNA together are clearly shown. In this figure, however, the wavy vertical arrows divide the part of the DNA molecule which is depicted into three sets of paired nucleotides. Reading the figure from left to right, the first set includes the complementary pairs GC, GC and CG; the second set, the pairs AT, GC and AT; and the third set, the pairs CG, TA and TA. In each set of pairs of three nucleotides the three bases in the upper strand, as illustrated, are complementary to the three bases in the lower strand. Each of these groups of three bases forms a *triplet*, thus the groups GGC, AGA and CTT form triplets complementary to CCG, TCT and GAA respectively. The information contained in a series of triplets in a DNA molecule is used for the synthesis of proteins.

```
-D-P-D-P-D|P-D-P-D-P-D|P-D-P-D-P-D-P-
   |     |     |     |     |     |     |     |     |
   G     G     C     A     G     A     C     T     T
   :     :     :     :     :     :     :     :     :
   C     C     G     T     C     T     G     A     A
   |     |     |     |     |     |     |     |     |
P-D-P-D-P-D|P-D-P-D-P-D-P-D|P-D-P-D-P-D-
```

(a)

```
-D-P-D-P-D-P-D-P-D-P-D-P-D-P-D-P-D-P-
   |     |     |     |     |     |     |     |     |
   G     G     C     A     G     A     C     T     T
   :     :     :     :     :     :     :     :     :
   C     C     G     U     C     U     G     A     A
   |     |     |     |     |     |     |     |     |
P-R   P-R   P-R   P-R   P-R   P-R   P-R   P-R   P-R
 (     (     (     (     (     (     (     (     (
 P     P     P     P     P     P     P     P     P
 (     (     (     (     (     (     (     (     (
 P     P     P     P     P     P     P     P     P
```

(b)

```
-D-P-D-P-D-P-D-P-D-P-D-P-D-P-D-P-D-P-
   |     |     |     |     |     |     |     |     |
   G     G     C     A     G     A     C     T     T
   :     :     :     :     :     :     :     :     :
   C     C     G     U     C     U     G     A     A
   |     |     |     |     |     |     |     |     |
P-R   P-R   P-R   P-R- P-R- P-R- P-R- P-R- P-R
 (     (     (     (
 P     P     P     P            (c)
 (     (     (     (
 P     P     P     P
```

FIG. 8.4   The formation of m-RNA: (a) part of the DNA molecule, (b) attachment of the complementary bases (as nucleotide phosphates) to one chain of DNA, (c) linking of the nucleotide units to form the m-RNA chain.

It is essential to remember in the first instance that proteins consist of long chains of amino acids joined together by peptide bonds. In any given proteins the number, type and sequence of amino acids in the chains is always constant and characteristic. It follows thus that the information which must be stored, relating to the composition of any given protein in the body must include —

(*a*) the number of amino acids present in the protein molecule;
(*b*) which ones these amino acids are; and
(*c*) the sequence in which they occur in the chain of the protein molecule.

Let us return for the moment to the structure of a portion of the DNA molecule as depicted in Fig. 8.4 and consider how this information could possibly be stored in such a structure. The only way in which it could be done, is by the arrangement of the purine and pyrimidine bases to form a meaningful *code*. Assume for a moment that every triplet of three bases forms a code word which denotes the name of a particular amino acid, for instance, GGC denotes proline, AGA denotes serine and CTT denotes glutamic acid. The upper strand of the DNA molecule represented in Fig. 8.4a now represents the genetic code for *three* amino acids in the *specific sequence*, proline — serine — glutamic acid. The three requirements relating to the storage of information for protein synthesis can thus be met in this manner; the information is there which relates to number, names and sequence of the amino acids.

The word *gene* is familiar to most of us and we know that it denotes a substance which is responsible for the hereditary transmission of different characteristics of our body. However, genes determine also the reproduction of cells within the tissues, the differentiation and function of these cells and all the biochemical events which underlie these processes. Since we can trace all these phenomena back to the synthesis of various structural proteins, stored proteins or enzymes, genes must relate to these considerations. In general terms that part of the DNA molecule which contains the genetic code required for the synthesis of a single protein or perhaps even a group of proteins, is a gene. The exact number of genes present in the nucleus of any particular cell is not known with certainty, but there are enough present to control the synthesis of some thousands of different proteins.

Transcription of genetic information

When the synthesis of a particular enzyme or protein is required it is essential, as a first step that the two chains which make up the double helix of the DNA molecule are loosened from one another and the genetic information contained in the arrangement of the purine and pyrimidine bases becomes exposed and thus available.

However, the actual protein synthesis takes place at the ribosomes, located on the endoplasmic reticulum in the cytoplasm of the cell, whereas the DNA is in the nucleus.

The medium for carrying the necessary information from the nucleus to the ribosomes is messenger-RNA (m-RNA). It is synthesized on the particular gene concerned and during this synthesis the relevant information is "transcribed on to it".

The first step in the synthesis of m-RNA is the formation of the nucleotides which contain the four bases adenine, guanine, cytosine and uracil. Once this has been done, each nucleotide is "activated" by converting it to the pyrophosphate form, i.e. two additional phosphate radicals are added to it, with the consequent formation of "high energy phosphate bonds". The necessary pyrophosphate group is transferred from ATP, which acts as donor, to the nucleotide. We could represent this simply as nucleoside phosphate (=nucleotide) + ATP = nucleoside triphosphate + AMP.

The "activated" nucleosides move into the appropriate positions opposite the exposed DNA chain, so that their bases can bind with the exposed *complimentary* bases on the DNA strand; as shown in Fig. 8.4b The student will remember that these bases will bind to one another in the already mentioned fixed complementary combinations (chapter 7), viz,

DNA-bases		*RNA-bases*
guanine	. . . .	cytosine
cytosine	. . . .	guanine
adenine	. . . .	uracil
thymine	. . . .	adenine

N.B. Uracil replaces thymine in RNA.

Once all the exposed bases on the gene concerned, have bound with their complementary ones, coming in for the synthesis of RNA, these latter bases will be arranged in the correct sequence *to form "code words" which correspond to the triplets on the strand of DNA concerned* (see Fig. 8.4b). These *corresponding* "code-words" or triplets, are known as *codons*.

The stage is set now for the final formation of the m-RNA molecule. All that needs to be done is to link up the nucleotides through their ribose and phosphate units, as shown in Fig. 8.4c and to remove the "activating" pyrophosphate groups. This is accomplished by the enzyme *RNA-polymerase*, and as fast as it occurs, so the m-RNA separates, as a distinct entity, from the strand of DNA.

The genetic information has been "transcribed" and the transcription consists of a strand of m-RNA containing the codons, or triplets corresponding to those on the original DNA chain, and in the correct sequence. The fragment of the m-RNA chain represented in Fig. 8.4c carries the "code-words" or *codons* CCG, UCU and GAA *which correspond to the* "code-words" GGC, AGA and CTT, representing the amino acids proline, serine and glutamic acid. Depending on the composition of the protein molecule to be synthesized the m-RNA can contain many thousands of these codons. The necessary information is thus "contained" in the RNA molecule, which then moves, in a manner as yet not clear, out of the nucleus to the ribosomes located on the endoplasmic reticulum where the actual protein synthesis will occur.

Translation of genetic information

The amino acids available for protein synthesis are present in solution in the cytoplasmic sap. The many hundreds or thousands of amino acids which occur in any protein molecule represent in fact a large accumulation of only about twenty different individual amino acids. Each one of these twenty amino acids is bound to a specific transfer-RNA (t-RNA) molecule, which bears the complementary triplet of bases for the amino acid concerned. This complementary triplet is known as the *anticodon*. The function of the t-RNA molecule is to bring the specific amino acid, represented by its anticodon, to the appropriate place on the m-RNA molecule (where the specific codon lies) so that the protein chain can be formed. Since the triplets of bases in the respective codons and anticodons are complementary, that is they may be envisaged as fitting together like the pieces of a jigsaw puzzle, only the appropriate amino acid can be brought into its correct place on the m-RNA molecule.

The ribosomes consisting largely of RNA, appear to act as supports upon which the protein molecule can be formed. They have been likened to the magnetic head of an ordinary tape-recorder which "reads" or "translates" the information on the "tape" of m-RNA as it passes over or through them. The analogy is a useful one and in terms of it we may consider protein synthesis as occurring in the following manner. The m-RNA molecule carrying the coded information about the protein to be synthesized arrives at the ribosome and either passes over or through it. Although perhaps fanciful we may consider it as having at one end a codon which represents "start synthesis" and at the other end another which represents "stop synthesis". As the signal to "start synthesis" passes over the appropriate part of the ribosome so the t-RNA molecules with their attached amino acids commence to be brought into contact with their corresponding codons on the moving m-RNA tape. The complementary base triplets bind with one another and the tape moves out of that particular point on the ribosome with the amino acids attached in the places they will occupy in the completed protein chain. When the end of the molecule is reached the signal to "stop synthesis" ends the further laying down of amino acids. All that has to occur now is for the amino acids, which have been arranged in the predetermined pattern, to combine with one another through the formation of peptide bonds and for the formed protein molecule to separate from its attachements on the m-RNA-t-RNA combination or "translated tape". We do in fact refer to these events as the *translation* of the information which was originally transcribed upon the m-RNA.

The formation of peptide bonds, as happens when the amino acids are arranged in sequence, requires energy. This is supplied by the compound *guanosine triphosphate* (GTP) an analogue of our more familiar ATP (see chapter 7). Large amounts of GTP accumulate in cells where active protein synthesis is in progress.

As soon as the protein chain is formed it is set free and the m-RNA, also freed of the t-RNA molecules, is at liberty to enter another ribosome where the translation process is repeated. A single strand of m-RNA can pass through several ribosomes simultaneously and hence produce several protein molecules at the same time. The clusters of ribosomes in which this occurs are often termed *polyribosomes*.

Cell division and the replication of genes

At the moment of fertilization of the mature ovum by a single spermatozoön, genetic material derived from both the male and the female is lumped together in a single cell, the fertilized ovum. From this cell, by means of repeated cell divisions and differentiation of cells into specialized tissues, will develop the complex organism which we call our bodies. In due course the genetic information contained within the nuclei of these cells will be transmitted to our offspring through the medium of an ovum or spermatozoön as the case may be.

In the majority of tissues in the body, cells are dying and are being continually replaced by living cells. This implies that in such tissues cell division is occurring constantly to cope with the normal wear-and-tear of tissues. Cell division commences in the nuclei of cells and embraces the following phenomena:

(a) duplication of all the genes present in the chromosomes;

(b) division of the two sets of genes between two newly-formed nuclei;

(c) division of the cell itself to form two daughter cells.

The entire process is known as *mitosis*. The duplication of the genes occurs by means of a process, which is basically similar to that in which m-RNA is formed on the DNA molecule. The initial step is opening of the DNA helix. Simultaneously, the deoxyribosenucleotides characteristic of the DNA molecule are formed, namely adenylic acid, thymidylic acid, guanylic acid and cytidylic acid. These then, following activation, move towards and bind with the complimentary bases now exposed on the two open strands of DNA. The enzyme DNA-polymerase links up the nucleotides to form the new DNA molecule. This then remains attached to the parent, upon which it has been formed at one particular point, until division of the nuclei when the parent and daughter molecules separate, giving each of the two newly-formed cells, its full complement of chromosomes.

The regulation of protein synthesis by control at the gene level

At the opening of the discussion on protein synthesis, we noted that when the DNA helix was opened, many other genes, besides the one controlling the synthesis of a particular protein, were exposed. These other genes can be "repressed", and only the one necessary for the particular protein synthesis will be allowed to function.

According to one of the most attractive explanations of this phenomenon, it is assumed that certain genes act as *regulatory genes*. These have the power to regulate the activity of all the other genes. They are apparently able to form a *repressor* substance, which acts on a small part of the helix adjacent to the genes which are to be used at any given moment. This small area of the helix is known as the *operator* and its function is to "activate" the genes concerned in the synthesis of particular proteins. The repressor inhibits the operator and thus the genes in question remain inactive. The group of genes controlled by an operator area is known as an *operon* and the individual genes within this group are called *structural genes*, since they control the synthesis of enzymes.

The repressor substance which is formed under the influence of the regulatory genes can itself be inhibited or activated. When it is inhibited, the operator is not suppressed and the structural genes can participate in the continuous synthesis of the enzymes concerned. If on the other hand the repressor substance is activated, it suppresses the operator at once and synthesis of the particular enzymes comes to a halt.

How is the repressor substance inhibited or activated? It is assumed that this occurs by means of a *negative feedback* exercised by one or more of the products of the reactions being catalyzed by the enzymes concerned. When the concentration of such products within the cell reaches a certain value the repressor substance is activated and the operator is suppressed. As the speed of the metabolic reactions concerned declines, so the concentration of the products formed falls correspondingly. The repressor is no longer activated and the operator is free to resume its previous activities.

This type of feedback system is of great importance in the regulation of, amongst other things, the intracellular concentrations of amino acids and the concentration of some of the intermediary products of protein, lipid and carbohydrate metabolism.

In the discussion immediately above mention was made only of the activation of a repressor substance and its return to an inactive state. Repressor substances may also be *inhibited*. In such instances the inhibitory control over the operator is removed and it is free to work at its full capacity. It is very likely that the steroid hormones act as inhibitors of certain repressors. When this type of inhibition of a repressor substance occurs we speak of *enzyme induction* or *de-repression*.

Hormonal regulation of enzyme production and activity

Although the anatomical distribution and the basic rate of production of enzymes is determined genetically, there must exist other regulatory mechanisms that can vary according to the momentary needs of the body. We have already discussed the local regulation of enzymatic activity. This is, however, limited to regulation according to local demands. Hormonal control, generally initiated by a negative feedback mechanism, is, however, a long-range mechanism, since the hormones are produced by glands distant from where they act. For instance, should the blood sugar level fall, the hormones adrenalin and glucagon, produced by the adrenal medulla and the islands of Langerhans in the pancreas respectively, are released and stimulate the breakdown of glycogen in liver cells to form more glucose and so to raise the blood sugar level. More will be said about hormonal regulation in chapter 12.

CHAPTER 9

The Digestion and Absorption of Nutrients

With the exception of oxygen, the substances necessary for growth and the maintenance of body functions are absorbed from the gastro-intestinal canal. Water, soluble mineral salts and ions are absorbed without any chemical change. Nutrients such as glucose, amino acids and fatty acids are generally present in the food we take as part of complex molecules such as carbohydrates, proteins and fats, which are degraded by the process of digestion to the simple products mentioned. Each living species forms complex molecules like proteins which are characteristic of the species concerned. The introduction of foreign proteins into the blood and tissue fluids can give rise to severe allergic reactions and in a few instances certain proteins of plant origin are frankly toxic. In this respect digestion serves a dual purpose. The degradation of foreign proteins to amino acids renders such proteins harmless. The amino acids which are released can, after absorption, be incorporated into the body's own specific proteins. Considerations such as this also apply to many of the complex carbohydrates and lipids. Oils of plant origin are degraded by digestion to fatty acids and glycerol. After absorption these products can be converted into the hard fats typical of the human or animal body.

The digestive degradation of large complex molecules occurs by hydrolysis catalysed by enzymes. The enzymes are either present in digestive secretions such as saliva, gastric juice or pancreatic juice or are present in the brush-borders of the cells lining the lumen of the small intestine. The digestive secretions mentioned have a very high water and mucus content. Both of these substances serve very important physiological functions in digestion. Both serve a lubricant function and facilitate processes such as swallowing. During its passage through the digestive tract the food is thoroughly mixed with the water of these secretions, thus permitting the access of enzymes to the surface of the food particles. Fatty substances pass into an emulsion which also facilitates enzyme attack. The water present naturally also makes it possible for the substances liberated by digestion to be absorbed, since these pass into solution, suspension or emulsion depending upon their physical properties. The presence of saliva in the swallowed food mass has the effect also of diluting irritant substances and of cooling down hot foods. Besides its lubricant function mucus plays a decidedly protective role. It protects the lining of the digestive tract against irritant substances, dilute acids and alkali's and protects the lining cells against the action of some of the powerful enzymes of digestion like pepsin and trypsin (see below).

Digestion in the mouth

Saliva, produced by the parotid, submaxillary and sublingual glands contains only one enzyme of digestion, notably *salivary amylase*, sometimes referred to by the obsolete name *ptyalin*. This enzyme hydrolyses the large starch molecules in our foods to smaller fragments known as dextrins and degrades these in turn to the disaccharide, maltose. (The name amylase has its origin in the Latin word for starch, amylum.) We have noted, in one of the previous chapters, that enzymes are remarkably pH dependant. The optimal *pH* for salivary amylase, is that of saliva, i.e. *6,0-7,0*. Salivary amylase has obviously little time to act upon starches, whilst the food is in the mouth, since mastication is generally brief. Once the food is swallowed, however, it continues to act upon the starches until its action is stopped by the very acid conditions pertaining in the stomach. This will happen once the swallowed food has become adequately mixed with gastric juice. The small amount of starch digestion which occurs in the mouth is evidenced by the fact that when a starch-containing substance like bread is chewed for any length of time it gradually acquires a sweetish taste due to the liberated maltose.

The secretion of saliva is a complex reflex process, initiated amongst other things by the presence of food in the mouth, by the process of mastication and by the sight and smell of foodstuffs.

Digestion in the stomach

The stomach is a temporary storage organ for ingested food and the pyloric sphinctre permits only the intermittent passage of small amounts of the foodmass into the small intestine, where the most important processes of digestion occur. During its sojourn in the stomach, the proteins in the foodmass are subjected to some fair degree of digestion. Gastric juice contains amongst other things, the enzymes *pepsin, rennin* and *lipase* and *hydrochloric acid* in watery solution. The enzymes are formed in the chief cells in the lining of the stomach, pepsin being formed as an inactive precursor, *pepsinogen*. Hydrochloric acid, formed in the parietal (or oxyntic) cells activates pepsinogen and the resulting pepsin is a relatively weak proteolytic enzyme. This name is applied to enzymes that specifically hydrolyse proteins. The product of pepsin digestion is a mixture of small polypeptide fragments of the original protein molecules.

Although *rennin*[1] is probably present in the gastric juice in variable amounts throughout one's life, it is only of importance to us in the infant stage. Its function is to bring about the coagulation of ingested milk. The digestive tract of the suckling child or animal is relatively short and undeveloped and many of the enzymes of digestion are not yet being produced in adequate quantity. Coagulation of the milk serves the purpose of slowing down its passage through the digestive tract, thus considerably aiding digestion and the absorption of the products of digestion. Rennin changes the major protein constituent of milk, *casein*, into insoluble curds of calcium paracaseinate in the presence of calcium ions (which are present in high concentration in milk). Other milk proteins, the milk fats and milk carbohydrates like lactose are trapped in the curds and their passage down the digestive tract is thus considerably retarded.

Gastric juice *lipase* (the name is derived from the Greek word for fat, *lipos*), like rennin, is probably of importance only in the suckling infant. It is a weak fat-splitting enzyme converting the milk butter-fats into glycerol and fatty acids.

As noted above, the digestion of starches continues for a while until the action of the salivary amylase is halted by the acidic gastric juice which slowly permeates the food mass in the stomach.

The *pH* of gastric juice lies between *1,5-3,0*. This low pH is due to the presence of hydrochloric acid. As we have just seen this compound activates pepsinogen. Since it is a strong acid it is capable of some hydrolysis of the chemical bonds present in starch and protein molecules, but probably more important is its ability to bring minerals such as calcium salts, phosphates and the trace elements, iron, copper, manganese, zinc and so on, into solution thus facilitating their absorption. This action constitutes a major digestive function of hydrochloric acid in the carnivorous animals, whose main source of calcium and phosphorus is the bones they ingest.

As mentioned earlier, hydrochloric acid is formed in the parietal cells of the gastric mucosa; and it forms according to the equation

$$H^+ + Cl^- \rightleftharpoons HCl$$

Chloride ions are readily available from the sodium chloride present in the tissue fluids. The hydrogen ions are produced from carbonic acid, by the action of the enzyme, *carbonic anhydrase*, according to the set of equations

$$H_2O + CO_2 \rightleftharpoons H_2CO_3$$
$$H_2CO_3 \rightleftharpoons H^+ + HCO_3^-$$

The bicarbonate ions can be returned to the tissue fluids in association with sodium ions from the sodium chloride just mentioned.

---

[1]Note the spelling of this name *rennin*. It is not to be confused with the enzyme *renin* (spelt with one 'n') produced in the kidneys (see chapter 12).

The secretion of gastric juice is governed by reflexes and by the hormone gastrin. As in the case of salivary secretion, the secretion of gastric juice can be prompted by the sight and smell of food. As food particles come into contact with certain receptors in the mouth, pharynx and gastric mucosa, so nerve reflexes are initiated leading to the secretion of gastric juice. As some of the ingested food mass reaches the pyloric region of the stomach, certain cells lining this area secrete the hormone, *gastrin,* into the blood stream. This hormone is conveyed by the blood to the fundus of the stomach where the zymogenic or chief cells are located and stimulates the secretion of a gastric juice rich in pepsinogen, lipase and rennin. About two litres of gastric juice are produced daily by the average adult, most of this being produced shortly before, during, or after meals.

We have noted that the stomach functions as a temporary reservoir for ingested food, and that the passage of this food through into the small intestine occurs intermittently. The passage of the ingesta into the duodenum is considerably retarded by the action of the hormone, *enterogastrone.* This hormone is produced by some of the cells lining the duodenum, when large amounts of fat pass into it from the stomach. The hormone is transported to the musculature of the stomach via the bloodstream and has an inhibitory action on the movements of the stomach wall. Since fat in large quantities can seriously impair the digestion of proteins and carbohydrates and interfere with the absorption of the products of this digestion, the value of this enterogastrone mechanism should be apparent.

Before leaving the topic of digestion in the stomach, we should take note of one vital function of the stomach, which although not strictly one of digestion, nevertheless involves the intervention of hydrochloric acid. Vitamin B_{12} (cyanocobalamine) is absorbed from the small intestine in the presence of an *intrinsic factor* produced by certain cells in the stomach. Hydrochloric acid is required for this process as well. In the event of poor production by the gastric mucosa of hydrochloric acid (achlorhydria) or of intrinsic factor, a vitamin B_{12} deficiency can arise leading to the appearance of *pernicious anaemia.*

Digestion in the small intestine

The most important processes of digestion take place in this structure; the digestive juices concerned being produced by the pancreas, liver and cells of the duodenum. Of these *pancreatic juice* is by far the most important since it contains all the enzymes of digestion which are of major importance, notably the proteolytic enzymes, *trypsin, chymotrypsin* and *carboxypeptidases A* and *B*; the starch splitting enzyme, *pancreatic amylase* and the lipolytic (fat-splitting) enzyme, *pancreatic lipase*. Besides these, it contains various *phospholipases* (acting upon phospholipids), ribonuclease (acting upon RNA), *nucleotidases* (acting upon nucleotides) and large amounts of sodium bicarbonate. The pancreatic juice passes into the lumen of the small intestine via the pancreatic duct. The cells of the mucosa of the duodenum and ileum contain in their brush borders enzymes such as *disaccharidases*, *weak lipases*, *proteases*, *peptidases*, *nucleotidases*, an *amylase* and they also produce the enzyme *enterokinase*. The powerful proteolytic enzymes, trypsin and chymotrypsin, are produced and secreted by the acinar cells of the pancreas in the inactive forms trypsinogen and chymotrypsinogen. This is necessary in order to prevent self-digestion. Once the pancreatic juice reaches the lumen of the small intestine trypsinogen is activated by the enzyme enterokinase. The very active trypsin which is formed also serves as the activator of chymotrypsinogen, converting it to chymotrypsin.

The glands of Brunner, present in the duodenal mucosa pour out large amounts of *mucus*, the purpose of which is to protect the intestinal mucosa against the acid of the gastric juice and the proteolytic actions of trypsin and chymotrypsin.

Bile contains no enzymes, yet it is extremely important for digestion. It contains amongst other things large amounts of *sodium bicarbonate*. This, together with the bicarbonate in the pancreatic juice, serves to neutralize the hydrochloric acid present in the chyme passing through from the stomach, thus providing an alkaline milieu in which the enzymes present in the pancreatic juice can operate efficiently. The optimal *pH* of these enzymes lies in the region of *8,0-8,5* this pH being assured by the bicarbonate ions as just described. The word *chyme* denotes the pulpy mixture of partially digested ingesta, and digestive juices moving from the stomach down into the small intestine.

Bile also contains fair amounts of *lecithin*. This phospholipid together with the bile acid salts, sodium taurocholate and sodium glycocholate is an important factor in the *emulsification* of fat present in the chyme. The importance of these compounds will be discussed in a moment.

Apart from these digestive functions, bile also serves as a route by which certain waste products of metabolism can be eliminated from the body, for instance the bile pigment *bilirubin* and *cholesterol*.

Bile is formed by the cells of the liver and is continually being discharged into the small bile ducts. It accumulates in the gall bladder, where it is temporarily stored, until required for digestion, and then passes into the duodenum via the bile duct.

Starch digestion, which commenced when saliva was mixed with the ingested food is completed in the small intestine by means of the amylase present in pancreatic juice. This enzyme also degrades the dextrans formed during starch digestion. The final product resulting from the action of amylase, is the disaccharide, maltose. This sugar is degraded to its constituent units by the disaccharidase, maltase, present in the brush-border of the cells lining the small intestine. Lactose present in milk, is degraded by lactase to its constituent units, glucose and galactose, while sucrose (cane sugar) is converted by sucrase into its constituents, glucose and fructose. Lactase and sucrase occur together with maltase in the site mentioned. The final products of the digestion of carbohydrates are thus the monosaccharides, *glucose, fructose* and *galactose*. These products are easily and rapidly absorbed from the small intestine into the blood-stream.

A number of complex carbohydrates present in our daily diet are undigestible. This means that enzymes capable of degrading them are not present in the digestive juices. Examples of these compounds are cellulose, hemicellulose, pectins, plant gums, various pentosans and so on. These substances nevertheless fulfill a very important physiological function. They constitute what is known as the "crude fibre" in our diet which lends bulk to the intestinal mass and stimulates peristaltic movements in the intestine. Diets low in fibre tend to be constipating, since this particular stimulus for peristalsis is diminished. On the other hand, certain food products with a high fibre content, like bran and dried fruits have a mildly laxative action, by increasing peristalsis. These undigestible complex carbohydrates are also important because they serve as sources of energy for the micro-organisms present in our large intestine. This large population of organisms is extremely important for our welfare, for in return for these undigested food residues, they provide us with many of the vitamins and amino acids which our tissues require.

The *proteins* present in the chyme have been partially degraded by pepsin present in the gastric juice. Any remaining proteins and the polypeptide products of digestion by pepsin are now fully degraded to amino acids by the concerted action of trypsin, chymotrypsin, the carboxypeptidases A and B and the peptidases present in the brush-borders of the cells in the mucosa of the small intestine. The *amino acids* which result from this digestion are absorbed into the bloodstream.

Although some digestion of *fats* occurs by gastric juice lipase in the stomach of infants, most digestion of these products occurs in the small intestine by means of pancreatic lipase. This enzyme, which is activated by the bile acid salts, sodium glycocholate and sodium taurocholate, can only act upon the fat in the chyme if it is present in an emulsified state. The student is referred back to chapter 5 for a discussion on emulsions. The formation of emulsions is greatly facilitated by the presence of compounds which possess a certain measure of solubility in both fats or oils and water. Such compounds, examples of which are the bile acid salts and lecithin, are known as emulsifying agents. By means of the various types of movements that occur in the small intestine, the fat present in the chyme is largely dispersed into the form of fine droplets. The agents mentioned bring these into a stable emulsion, which provides a large area of tiny fat droplets for the enzyme pancreatic lipase to act upon. About thirty per cent of the ingested fat is degraded by lipase into a mixture of *diglycerides, monoglycerides, fatty acids* and *glycerol*. The mono- and diglycerides also have emulsifying properties and promote the further emulsification of fat. The remaining undigested fat is mostly absorbed from the small intestine into the lymphatics in the form of this finely divided emulsion.

The commonly used household detergents act as emulsifying agents and so do our toilet soaps. All these substances have molecules, part of which are characteristically more soluble in water (hydrophilic) and part of which have a greater affinity for fats and oils (lipophylic).

If the fatty acids liberated during fat digestion are of short chain length, e.g. butyric acid and hexanoic acids, derived from butter fats, they can be absorbed directly into the bloodstream since they are reasonably water soluble. Those of medium and long chain length, which constitute most of the fatty acids present in our dietary fats are either absorbed in the above mentioned emulsion or associate with the bile acid salts to form hydrophilic complexes which are absorbed along with the other products of fat digestion.

The phospholipids present in our diet are generally degraded by phospholipases present in the pancreatic juice. Any fatty acids liberated by this process are absorbed as mentioned above.

Nucleoproteins present in the diet are initially hydrolysed to nucleic acids and proteins in the small intestine. The liberated nucleic acids are degraded by pancreatic juice ribonuclease and deoxyribonuclease to a mixture of nucleotides. These in turn are hydrolysed by nucleotidases to yield *nucleosides* and *phosphoric acid* which are absorbed.

The hormonal control of the digestive secretions

We have already taken note of the role of the hormone *gastrin* in the secretion of the gastric juice. It remains for us to consider the hormonal control of the digestive juices secreted into the small intestine. The composition and secretion of the pancreatic juice is regulated to a large extent by the combined action of two hormones, *secretin* and *pancreozymin*. These hormones are produced by various cells in the mucosa of the small intestine and are liberated into the bloodstream when the acid chyme together with some of the products of protein digestion by pepsin passes into the small intestine. The release of pancreozymin is also stimulated to a lesser extent by the presence of carbohydrates and fat in the chyme. These hormones are transported via the blood-stream to the acinar cells of the pancreas. Secretin stimulates the production of a watery pancreatic juice very rich in sodium bicarbonate, while pancreozymin stimulates the production of a juice rich in the various enzymes already mentioned in connection with pancreatic juice.

It is very likely that secretin also stimulates the production of bile by the parenchymal cells of the liver. The main stimulus for the continuous secretion of bile by these cells appears to be bile acid salts reabsorbed from the intestinal tract. These products, which play a major role in fat digestion and absorption are being continually secreted and are reabsorbed in association with fatty acids and fat emulsions. This continuous secretion and reabsorption is often referred to as the *entero-hepatic* circulation of the bile acid salts.

As seen earlier bile is temporarily stored in the gall-bladder. During its stay here a certain amount of the water present in it is reabsorbed through the gall-bladder mucosa into the blood-stream and the bile thus undergoes a measure of concentration. When chyme containing fat enters the small intestine, certain cells in the mucosa of this structure are stimulated to form and secrete the hormone, *cholecystokinin* into the blood-stream. On reaching the gall-bladder this hormone stimulates contraction of the musculature of the gall-bladder wall and relaxation of the sphinctre of Oddi, thus bringing about emptying of the gall-bladder into the duodenum. About 600ml of bile are released into the small intestine daily. It is thought by some that the pancreozymin and cholecystokinin actions are inherent in a single hormone often designated as cholecystokinin-pancreozymin.

It is also believed by some that the formation of the enzymes of digestion characteristic of the cells of the small intestine is stimulated by a hormone named *enterocrinin*. This hormone is believed to be formed and released into the blood-stream by certain cells present in the mucosa of the small intestine.

The absorption of nutrients from the alimentary canal

The majority of the products of digestion are absorbed in the small intestine. Some water and ethanol (if it is consumed) are absorbed in the stomach. The mucosa of the small intestine is extensively folded and bears millions of microscopic finger-like projections known as the *villi*, each being covered with mucosal cells. The villi in turn bear even tinier finger-like projections known as *microvilli*. Each villus contains an arteriole, a network of capillaries, a venule and a lymph vessel (the name *villus* is a Latin one denoting shaggy hair). The fact that the mucosa is extensively folded and still further elevated into villi and microvilli increases its effective surface area to about 550 square metres, thus presenting a large surface on which absorption can take place. When the acid chyme reaches the cells of the mucosa of the small intestine, some of these form and release the hormone, *villikinin*, into the blood-stream. This hormone stimulates movement of the villi, thus increasing the flow of blood and lymph through these structures and thereby facilitating the removal of absorbed nutrients.

Absorption of nutrients occurs largely through the medium of *active transport* mechanisms. These mechanisms are in some instances specific for given compounds, e.g. glucose or for groups of compounds, e.g. basic, neutral or acidic amino acids. In some instances their function is facilitated by the presence of certain co-factors. For instance the absorption of iron depends upon the presence of vitamin C (ascorbic acid), while the absorption of amino acids depends upon the presence of vitamin B_6 (pyridoxine). The absorption of calcium is stimulated by the hormone, 1,25 dihydroxy-cholecalciferol (1,25-DHC).

Water soluble substances such as the monosaccharides, the amino acids, short chain fatty acids and glycerol pass into the blood-stream after absorption and pass via the portal circulation to the liver.

Mono- and diglycerides and long chain fatty acids are re-combined in the mucosal cells of the small intestine to form triglycerides. These molecules associate with small amounts of cholesterol, phospholipids and proteins to form tiny fatty droplets known as *chylomicrons*. These particles pass into the lymphatics and ultimately gain entry into the blood-stream via the thoracic duct. After a meal rich in fat, the thoracic duct lymph has a distinctly milky appearance due to the presence of a large amount of chylomicrons. Such lymph is often called *chyle* (from the Greek, *chulos*, a juice produced by digestion).

The functions of the large intestine

This structure has a large absorbing surface through which water and many water soluble products can be absorbed. It is here that the chyme moving through from the small intestine is finally converted into the faeces. The large intestine supports a very large population of *micro-organisms* which live in symbiosis with us. Most of these are bacteria, but fair numbers of protozoa, yeasts and fungi are also present. These organisms live upon the undigested food residues and in turn provide us with certain vitamins, essential amino acids and fatty acids. For instance, most of the *vitamin K* which we absorb from the digestive tract derives from these organisms.

The faeces form largely as a result of the activity of these organisms. They consist of undigested food residues, dead organisms, water and the products of the action of these organisms on the food residues. The characteristic colour of the stools is due to the presence of urobilin formed from urobilinogen by bacterial action. Some amino acids are converted to volatile amines; the amino acid tryptophan is converted into the foul smelling indole and skatole while phenylalanine and tyrosine are degraded to phenol and cresol. The sulphur containing amino acids cysteine and methionine give rise to hydrogen sulphide and other sulphides, while undigested fats are converted into various unpleasant smelling aldehydes and fatty acids. All of these compounds contribute towards the typical odour of the stools. Gases like carbon dioxide, hydrogen and methane (CH_4) arise from the action of bacteria on various undigested carbohydrates.

One of the main functions of the rectum is that of water absorption. It is here that the faeces assume their final physical form. Only enough water is left in them to facilitate defaecation. The efficiency of water absorption in the rectum and large intestine is readily appreciated if one thinks for a while of the rapid and thorough desiccation the stools undergo during constipation. Defaecation becomes a difficult and often painful matter. Water soluble substances are readily absorbed from the rectum and drugs are often administered by this route in the form of enemas or suppositories, where swallowing is difficult or vomiting is severe and continuous.

CHAPTER 10

Metabolism

The products of digestion are absorbed from the small intestine into the blood or the lymph in the case of the products of fat digestion. In either event they are distributed to the body tissues by the blood circulation. Since all blood flow leaving the intestine passes through the liver the latter receives most of the absorbed nutrients. The liver is the site of the greatest *metabolic* activity in the body. The word *metabolism* describes the changes which these nutrient substances are subjected to in living tissues, and it embraces two major areas of such changes; *anabolism*, the building up of larger molecules and structural entities, and *catabolism*, which is the degradation of these larger molecules for energy production or for supplying simple substances for further anabolic events. In the liver then, some of the absorbed nutrients are immediately converted into larger molecules for *storage* purposes, e.g. glucose and amino acids may be converted into glycogen and proteins respectively; some of the absorbed products may be used at once for the production of other *important and necessary substances*, e.g. some of the fatty acids may be converted into the bile salts; and some of these nutrients, like glucose, may be used immediately to provide for the liver's own energy requirements. However, metabolism is not limited to the liver: it does take place in most of the tissues of the body although not at the same rate in some of them.

The metabolism in the carbohydrates, proteins and fats takes place through the medium of a set series of reactions which are specific in each of the three instances (Fig. 10.1). Each specific set of reactions, known as a *metabolic pathway* or *cycle*, as the case may be, is so designed that if a given nutrient enters it at a determined point of entry, it will be transformed through a series of degradation products, many of which can be used in physiologically useful side reactions, to find a product which is in turn of great physiological significance. The reactions comprising each particular transformation are so linked with one another that the reaction products pass smoothly and rapidly from one reaction into the next. In the majority of instances the reactions in each pathway or cycle are fully reversible. This permits the back-and-forth shuttling of metabolites, thus making possible the fact that anabolism and catabolism of a particular major nutrient occur through the same series of reactions. The word *metabolite* refers

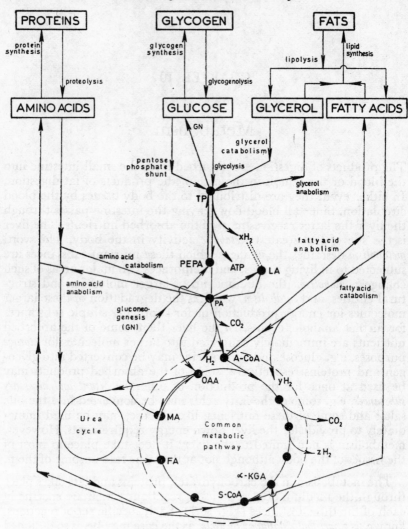

FIG. 10.1   Schematic representation of the main metabolic pathways (TP = triose phosphates, PEPA = phospho-enol pyruvic acid, PA = pyruvic acid, A-CoA = acetyl-CoA, OAA = oxalacetic acid, MA = malic acid, FA = fumaric acid, S-CoA = succinyl-CoA, α-KGA = alpha keto glutaric acid).

to any intermediary product taking part in the series of reactions constituting a metabolic pathway or cycle. Since each particular reaction in a pathway or cycle is catalyzed by its own specific enzyme, often with its own particular co-factors, these pathways represent a considerable economy of available metabolic resources. Furthermore space is necessarily limited within any cell. Since cells very often have to accommodate large molecules of stored nutrients, or other paraphernalia connected with their physiological functions, economy of space is obviously of prime importance. The advantages of having a single metabolic cycle or pathway perform a number of physiologically important functions are manifold.

Each of the pathways representing the major anabolic or catabolic events in the metabolism of carbohydrates, fats and proteins incorporates at least one step in which *energy* can be generated. Such steps involve the oxidation of the metabolites entering the reactions involved. The term *oxidation* in this case refers to the complex series of reactions consisting of the removal of two hydrogen atoms from each molecule of the metabolite concerned (*dehydrogenation*) and causing them to combine with an atom of oxygen (*the actual* oxidation).

The overall process yields energy and a molecule of water. As the oxidation proceeds, so a portion of the energy is "taken up" and held in store in the *high-energy phosphate bonds of ATP*. While the dehydrogenation step is an integral part of the major metabolic pathway concerned, the actual oxidation of hydrogen and the concomittant synthesis of ATP occur in a set of side-reactions known as the *respiratory chain* (or *electron transfer pathway*).

We noted above that the set of transformations occurring in each metabolic pathway terminated with the formation of a physiologically significant end-product. These end-products, for instance *pyruvic acid* in the case of carbohydrate metabolism, and *acetyl-coenzyme A* in the case of fatty acids, are channelled into a single common metabolic pathway in which they are again used to maximum advantage. In the end, apart from any excess of water, nutrients or metabolites which may be excreted, the only waste products which leave the body as a result of this vast economic metabolic activity are carbon dioxide, and urea (the form in which ammonia is eliminated).

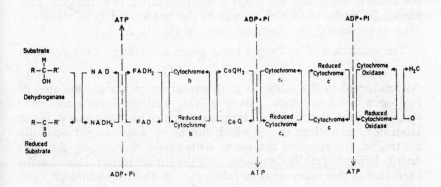

FIG. 10.2 The electron transport system (respiratory chain, oxidative phosphorylation).

The various metabolic pathways (Fig. 10.1) are thus joined together by the common metabolic pathway, as well as through other channels. In the first instance, what actually happens in any one of these pathways or cycles will depend on the type of cell where these events are taking place, and the metabolic requirements of that particular cell at any given moment. For instance glucose may be converted into glycogen if the cell is a liver parenchymal cell or skeletal muscle cell, or it may be converted into pyruvic acid with the concomitant production of energy, if this is the need that has to be met in these or other cells at a given moment. Its constituent carbon, hydrogen and oxygen atoms may alternatively be diverted via a side-pathway into the synthesis of glycerol for the production of stored triglycerides if this is the primary object of the cell's metabolic activity at that moment.

In this chapter the pathways will be presented mainly in a schematic manner. The student should endeavour to understand the purpose of the sequence of reactions involved in each pathway, and the functions of the pathway as a whole, rather than attempt to memorise each particular scheme with all its attendant detail. Since metabolism is a highly integrated process, involving the integration and concerted activity of all these pathways, the student should after mastering the purpose and functions of each pathway, endeavour to bring it into meaningful relation with the other metabolic pathways.

The respiratory chain (or electron transfer pathway)

The primary purpose of each metabolic pathway is to produce energy, since all chemical and physiological events which occur in cells ultimately require energy. As noted above most of this energy is formed during the sequence of reactions which take place in the respiratory chain, and leads to the final oxidation of hydrogen. This metabolic pathway, which occurs in the mitochondria of all living cells, is presented in schematic form in Fig. 10.2.

The oxidation of hydrogen takes place according to the reaction

$$2H_2 + O_2 = 2H_2O$$

As conducted in the laboratory, this reaction entails the burning of hydrogen in the presence of oxygen. The resulting flame is intensely hot, indicating the release of large amounts of heat as energy. If the laboratory conditions under which this takes place are not carefully controlled, the reaction can occur with explosive violence, the heat energy being forcefully dissipated into the surroundings. It is obvious then that if this reaction is to take place in cells, it should proceed in such a manner that the rate and the production of heat are carefully regulated, and that the heat produced is not dissipated uselessly, but harnessed for cell work. An added advantage would be the trapping and storage of some of this energy in a readily available form.

Fig. 10.2 portrays eight discrete steps through which the oxidation of hydrogen proceeds gently in a stepwise manner. Each step is catalyzed by its own particular enzyme; a *dehydrogenase* in each case, except in the final step where the enzyme concerned is *cytochrome oxidase*, which unites hydrogen and oxygen atoms. The synthesis of ATP occurs at three points on the pathway and for every two atoms of hydrogen which are metabolized in this manner, three molecules of ATP are formed. The energy converted into ATP this way represents about 45% of the total energy released by the respiratory chain, the other 55% being released as heat into the cellular space.

So much for the important general functioning of this metabolic pathway. We must now consider, albeit briefly, some of the detail involved. The first step shown in the above figure entails the removal of two hydrogen atoms from a substrate. This reaction is not strictly speaking part of the respiratory chain, but rather part of one of the major metabolic pathways. The events in the respiratory chain commence with the transfer of the hydrogen atoms to the co-enzyme NAD, which is then converted to $NADH_2$.

It will be remembered that co-enzymes are compounds which assist enzymes by removing the products of an enzyme catalized reaction, or by providing these when the reaction occurs in the reverse direction. Since the transfer of hydrogen atoms down this chain involves essentially the various co-enzymes shown, it is customary to portray only these and not the enzymes which actually catalyze each discrete step in the oxidation of hydrogen. The removal of the hydrogen atoms from NAD involves the transfer of the two hydrogen atoms on the next co-enzyme FAD, with the resulting formation of $FADH_2$. The transfer of hydrogen atoms to the further co-enzymes proceeds smoothly through the co-enzymes cytochrome b, co-enzyme Q, and cytochromes c_1 and c_2 until by the action of cytochrome oxidase the two hydrogen atoms are finally bound to oxygen with the production of water. This water represents most of the water formed during metabolic processes. We refer to it as *metabolic water* and it is of great importance in maintaining the water balance in the body.

Although the majority of dehydrogenases in the major metabolic pathways are linked to the respiratory chain through the first co-enzyme NAD, there are a few that are linked to the chain through FAD. We shall encounter them later in this discussion, but it is important to note at this stage, that in terms of what is portrayed in Fig. 10.2, only two molecules of ATP will then be formed for every two atoms of hydrogen entering the respiratory chain. In the normal course of events the first molecule of ATP forms when hydrogen atoms are passed on from NAD to FAD. When they enter the chain at the point of FAD, however, this site of ATP synthesis is by-passed.

The efficient oxidation of hydrogen by this pathway depends on the constant availability of oxygen. Oxygen dependant processes of this nature are referred to as *aerobic* processes. If for any reason the supply of oxygen is inadequate or hindered, the oxidation of hydrogen cannot be completed (see later). This blocks the acceptance of further hydrogen atoms by NAD, thus seriously impairing the function of the dehydrogenase to which the respiratory chain is linked. This in effect blocks the major metabolic pathway concerned at this particular point, with generally catastrophic results, since life processes are highly *energy dependant*.

The synthesis of ATP during the oxidation of hydrogen occurs according to the reaction

$$\text{ADP} + \text{Pi} + \text{energy} \rightleftharpoons \text{ATP}$$

where Pi represents a phosphate ion. Exactly how the phosphate ion is activated and bound to ADP is not known with certainty, but it is believed that certain carrier molecules are involved. Since this process involves phosphorylation of ADP (and the name means simply an addition of a phosphate radicle to a substance) in the presence of the oxidation of hydrogen (providing the energy shown in the equation above) we refer to this type of synthesis of ATP as the *oxidative phosphorylation* of ADP. We also say that this trapping of energy in the form of ATP is *coupled* to the oxidation of hydrogen. Certain agents are known which prevent the phosphorylation of ADP by the reaction shown above. These agents are known as *uncoupling agents* since they divorce the synthesis of ATP from the oxidation of hydrogen. When this happens, less than the normal 45 per cent of the energy formed from the oxidation of hydrogen is trapped as ATP and more is made available as free heat, thus increasing the free heat output of the system significantly. It is possible that the thyroid hormones, thyroxine and tri-iodothyronine, act in this manner (see chapter 12) since they stimulate metabolic processes by increasing the amount of free heat available.

Other sources of ATP

Although most of the supply of ATP available to a cell is formed in the mitochondria by the oxidative phosphorylation of ADP, significant amounts of ATP are also formed elsewhere during the course of some of the reactions in various metabolic pathways. Such reactions are themselves not oxygen dependant (although the overall functioning of the pathway may be) and involve an anaerobic synthesis of ATP. Since this type of synthesis involves the transfer of a phosphate radical from a phosphorylated metabolite or substrate directly on to ADP, the process is often referred to as a *substrate-level phosphorylation* of ADP. We shall encounter a number of important examples of this shortly, but at the moment, merely to illustrate the point the following example should suffice:

$$\text{Creatine phosphate} + \text{ADP} \rightleftharpoons \text{creatine} + \text{ATP}$$

This reaction is an important one in the biochemistry of muscle contraction, serving as a means for the regeneration of ATP from creatine phosphate. The enzymes which catalyze this type of reaction are known as *phosphokinases* and in this particular case the enzyme concerned is creatine phosphokinase (CPK).

Since the primary function of the major metabolic pathways is to provide hydrogen for oxidation and energy production, it is perhaps appropriate to consider the catabolism of the major nutrients, the carbohydrates, fats and proteins first, before we consider the anabolic side of the cell's metabolic activities.

The catabolism of carbohydrates

This basically involves three closely related sets of catabolic reactions, which we name glycogenolysis, glycolysis and the pentose-monophosphate shunt.

Glycogenolysis

The name implies the breakdown of glycogen (see Fig. 10.3). (The suffix, -lysis, occurs frequently in many words used in the biological sciences, and takes its origin from the Greek, *lusis*, to loosen or disrupt.) More specifically it embraces the series of reactions leading to the conversion of storage glycogen to glucose-6-phosphate. Glycogen is mainly stored in the parenchymal cells of the liver, muscle cells and the cells of adipose tissue and glycogenolysis is therefore a characteristic feature of these tissues. The process is a complex one involving hydrolysis of the glycogen molecule with concomitant phosphorylation of the glucose units as they are being set free, to form glucose-1-phosphate. One of the enzymes involved in this process is *glycogen phosphorylase*, which is activated by the hormones *adrenalin* and *glucagon*, via a complex cascade mechanism as described in chapter 8. The action of adrenalin, which is mainly on the breakdown of muscle glycogen, is shortlived, while that of glucagon is of relatively long duration and mainly upon the breakdown of liver glycogen. The glucose-1-phosphate which is formed is then converted rapidly into glucose-6-phosphate.

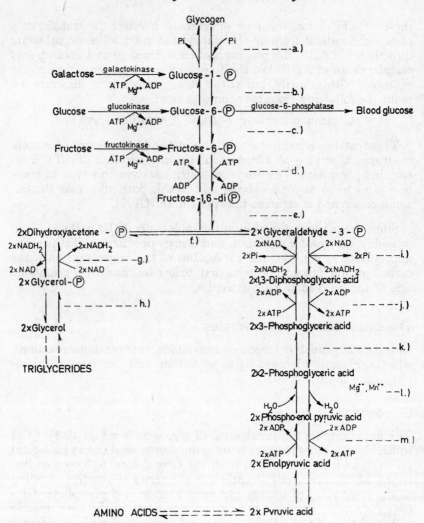

FIG. 10.3 The Embden-Meyerhof pathway or glycolytic pathway. (The names of enzymes: (a) glycogen phosphorylase, (b) phospho-glucomutase, (c) phospho-hexose isomerase, (d) phospho-fructo kinase, (e) aldolase, (f) triose phosphate isomerase, (g) glycerol phosphate dehydrogenase, (h) glycerol kinase, (i) glyceraldehyde phosphate dehydrogenase, (j) phosphoglyceric acid kinase, (k) phosphoglycero mutase, (l) enolase, (m) pyruvate kinase).

Glycolysis

Glycolysis means the breakdown of glucose and it covers the transformation of glucose-6-phosphate to pyruvic acid, with the simultaneous production of energy. The pathway, shown in Fig. 10.3, is often referred to as the *glycolytic cycle* or the *Embden-Meyerhof pathway.*

The entry of monosaccharides into the glycolytic cycle

As can be seen from Fig. 10.3, there are points of entry present in the cycle for glucose, fructose and galactose. In order to enter the cycle each of these monosaccharides has first to be phosphorylated, as in the reaction

$$\text{glucose} + \text{ATP} = \text{glucose-6-phosphate} + \text{ADP}$$

As can be seen, the source of the phosphate group transferred on to glucose is ATP. One molecule of ATP is thus used up. The enzyme that catalyzes the reaction is *glucokinase*, and it requires magnesium ions for efficient action. Fructose and galactose are similarly phosphorylated, the enzymes concerned being fructokinase and galactokinase respectively.

The hormone, *insulin*, stimulates the passage of glucose from the blood into the cells of many tissues, notably muscle tissue. It appears to enhance the passage of glucose across cell membranes and hence to facilitate the phosphorylation step, leading to the formation of glucose-6-phosphate. Insulin is not necessary for the passage of glucose across the membranes of liver, heart or brain cells. The disease *diabetes mellitus* is characterised by a deficiency of insulin, and in this disease the passage of glucose into many insulin-dependant tissues is seriously disturbed.

Glucose-6-phosphate occupies a key position in the glycolytic cycle. Not only is it the point at which glucose can enter the cycle, but it represents a form in which glucose can also be readily converted to glycogen in liver, muscle or adipose tissue (see later in the chapter), and if it happens to be formed from liver glycogen, be readily converted into free glucose which passes into the blood stream to maintain the blood glucose level.

Branching of the glycolytic cycle —
Energy production and a link with fat metabolism

The formation of *fructose-1,6-diphosphate* requires the expenditure of one further molecule of ATP. This substance is split, in the following reaction into two closely related and readily *interconvertible* triose phosphates (viz, dihydroxy acetone phosphate or glyceraldehyde phosphate).

The pathway must permit the maximum possible use of the compounds forming in it, thus if the primary purpose of glucose catabolism at any moment is to form glycerol for fat synthesis, then this interconversion makes it possible for the formation of two molecules of *dihydroxy-acetone phosphate*, and thus two molecules of glycerol from the original fructose-1,6-diphosphate. If on the other hand the primary goal of glycolysis is, at any given moment, energy production, then this interconversion will ensure that two molecules of *glyceraldehyde-3-phosphate* will be formed. In either event the six carbon atoms of the original hexoses are still very much in the cycle but are moving down one of the two branches, depending on metabolic requirements, in the form of two molecules of one of the triose phosphates.

ATP production in glycolysis

When we look at the transformation of glyceraldehyde-3-phosphate to pyruvic acid we must bear in mind that at each step, two molecules of a particular metabolite are involved. This should be apparent from the previous discussion. The immediate important implication of this is a doubling up of the *yield* of ATP that is formed in the rest of the cycle. Two molecules of glyceraldehyde-3-phosphate are obtained from each glucose molecule and are converted to two molecules of 3-phospho-glyceric acid, hence two molecules of ATP are in fact formed. This cancels out the ATP expenditure that occurred earlier in the cycle. Two pairs of hydrogen atoms are then shuttled into the respiratory chain for oxidation to water and energy and the potential *yield of ATP* is thus $2 \times 3 = 6$ molecules.

During the final steps of the glycolytic cycle 2 molecules of 3-phosphoglyceric acid are converted via 2-phospho-glyceric acid and phospho-enolpyruvic acid to two molecules of pyruvic acid. These rather formidable names are not nearly as important as the fact that these reactions permit the formation at substrate level of *two further molecules of ATP*. Thus *the conversion of one molecule of* either *glucose* or fructose *to two molecules of pyruvic acid*, leads to the generation of a considerable amount of energy. Part of this energy *can* be trapped in the form of *eight molecules of ATP*.

The metabolic fate of pyruvic acid

A number of very important metabolic fates await the pyruvic acid which is formed (Fig. 10.4). Firstly, as we shall see shortly, it can be converted to *lactic acid*. It can also be converted into either *oxalacetic acid* or *acetyl co-enzyme A* and enter the final common pathway of metabolism in either form. During the course of its transformations in this cycle a further considerable yield of energy and ATP is obtained (see later). Furthermore pyruvic acid can be re-converted to *glycogen* or it can be converted into the amino acid *alanine* and pass into the sphere of protein metabolism. A glance at Fig. 10.1 will show that if pyruvic acid is in fact converted to acetyl co-enzyme A, it can pass into the synthesis of fatty acids and hence stored triglycerides. The formation of pyruvic acid represents thus a point of junction of all the major metabolic pathways. The catabolism of glucose takes place in the cytoplasm of the cell, but many of the transformations which pyruvic acid can undergo take place in the mitochondria. Considerable amounts of pyruvic acid probably diffuse continuously into these structures for the purposes mentioned.

Maintenance of the blood sugar level

We must return for a moment to glucose-6-phosphate, where we started this particular discussion. The statement was made that in the liver glucose-6-phosphate is formed by the process of glycogenolysis. Further hydrolysis of glucose-6-phosphate is carried out by the enzyme glucose-6-phosphatase, of which the liver contains large concentrations. It ensures that a very large part of the liver glycogen is converted to glucose, which after passing into the blood will be used by all the other tissues of the body. Other tissues of the body have little of this enzyme, and consequently cannot release glucose into the blood stream in the same manner. The normal limits of blood sugar concentration are 0,8-1,2g/l.

Glycolysis in muscle tissue

Muscle tissue uses its glycogen stores in a rather special way. During muscle contraction glycogenolysis commences and proceeds as already outlined. The glucose-6-phosphate which is formed passes into the glycolytic cycle and is rapidly converted into pyruvic acid and energy, part of which is trapped as ATP, as just explained. At this stage the process is *aerobic* in that oxygen is freely available for the combustion of hydrogen atoms. In the resting state much of the oxygen in muscle fibres is bound to myohaemoglobin and some of it is in solution in the cytoplasm of the muscle cells, and in the tissue fluids surrounding them. As the muscle starts contracting, so the oxygen which is immediately available, is consumed in the combustion of hydrogen atoms derived from glyceraldehyde-3-phosphate and ATP is produced.

If oxygen is used at a rate faster than it can reach the interior of the muscle fibres from the tissue fluids, hydrogen atoms will not be oxidized in the respiratory chain, and the glycolytic cycle will be effectively blocked at the glyceraldehyde-3-phosphate step. Production of energy and ATP will consequently fall off rapidly and the efficiency of muscle contraction will become seriously impaired.

To ease matters some ATP can be generated from the large amounts of creatine phosphate present in muscle tissue according to the equation

$$\text{creatine phosphate} + \text{ADP} \rightleftharpoons \text{creatine} + \text{ATP}$$

A point is reached, however, where even the creatine phosphate must be replenished, by the reverse of the reaction shown above.

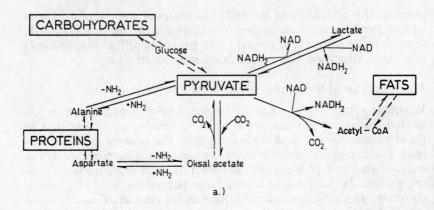

a.)

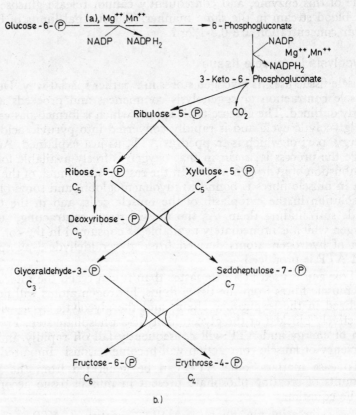

b.)

FIG. 10.4 (a) The metabolic fates of pyruvic acid, (b) The pentose monophosphate shunt.

It is obvious that some way of disposing of the hydrogen atoms must be found to clear the cycle once more, and to enable the ATP formed in the penultimate step of glycolysis to be produced. Assistance in this respect is readily available in muscle tissue in the form of the enzyme lactic dehydrogenase. The hydrogen atoms are transferred by this enzyme on to pyruvic acid that has been formed during the early stages of contraction, with the consequent formation of lactic acid. The lactic acid diffuses out of the muscle cell into the tissue fluids and is transported away from the muscle via the blood circulation.

The hydrogen atoms are thus removed from the muscle cells in the form of lactic acid, as fast as they are stripped off glyceraldehyde 3-phosphate. Glycolysis is free to continue right down to pyruvic acid and to produce ATP in the penultimate step. Creatine phosphate can be resynthesized and muscle contraction can continue smoothly and efficiently. The mechanism just described enables glycolysis to take place in muscle tissue in the presence of little oxygen; in other words under largely *anaerobic* conditions. Initially then as muscle contraction commences, glycolysis is an aerobic process, but rapidly becomes anaerobic as the available oxygen is being consumed. A prerequisite for the continued efficient contraction of the muscle fibres is the rapid removal of the accumulating lactic acid. Athletic training, exercise and the resulting fitness improve amongst other things the blood circulation in muscle tissue, contributing thus to the efficient removal of lactic acid and hence lead to the performance of more efficient muscular work.

When oxygen is again available lactic acid can be reconverted into pyruvic acid and hydrogen atoms. This mainly happens in the liver where the pyruvic acid can re-enter the glycolytic pathway and the hydrogen atoms can be disposed of by the usual means by the respiratory chain in the mitochondria of the liver cells.

It should be noted that lactic acid is not a mere waste product but exerts the following effects which are most relevant to the whole topic of muscle physiology and the physiology of fitness:

(i) it dissociates in solution yielding lactate ions and hydrogen ions;

(ii) this tends to lower the pH of the muscle tissue fluids and capillary blood.

The general effects of this are to —

(a) bring about dilatation of the blood vessels, thus increasing blood flow;

(b) stimulate the centres in the brain regulating cardio-vascular function and thus improving the blood circulation throughout the body;

(c) stimulate the centres in the brain concerned with respiration, thus promoting gas exchange in the lungs;

(d) depress the rate at which nerve impulses reach the muscle tissue.

This tends to slow down muscle contractions and contributes to the general phenomenon of fatigue, a mechanism which is intended to prevent over-exertion and the straining of muscle function beyond physiological limits.

The pentose monophosphate shunt

The word shunt denotes a deviation on to a side track. This short pathway constitutes a series of reactions into which glucose-6-phosphate can be diverted, the purpose being to form a variety of chemicals which can be used to meet various physiological needs. Some of these products can re-enter the glycolytic cycle at certain points and the shunt provides a means by which some of the steps of glycolysis can be by-passed. The pathway is presented in schematic form in Fig. 10.4b. The main functions of the pathway may be summarized as follows:

(a) it serves as the source of *ribose* and *deoxyribose* for the synthesis of RNA and DNA and various nucleotides like ATP;

(b) it provides hydrogen atoms and carbon dioxide for the *synthesis* of *fatty acids*; and

(c) it is coupled to the system responsible for the *reduction of methaemoglobin* in the erythrocytes, providing hydrogen atoms for this system.

The catabolism of fats

The body fat stores represent a compact source of nutrients which can be drawn upon to yield considerably more energy than the carbohydrates or proteins. Stored fat is deposited in characteristic areas in the body, often referred to as the fat depots. The fats which are laid down in these areas are triglycerides which contain as their fatty acid constituents, mainly long chain fatty acids like stearic acid, palmitic acid and oleic acid. These fatty acids represent the major energy-yielding components of the stored fats. The first step in the utilization of stored body fats is *lipolysis*, that is, the hydrolysis of these triglycerides by the enzyme *adipose tissue lipase* to yield glycerol and fatty acids. The activity of this enzyme, and hence the process of lipolysis, is stimulated by adrenalin. The liberated fatty acids are transported via the blood stream in combination with certain plasma proteins to the various body tissues.

The glycerol which is liberated can either be re-used for fat synthesis or may reach the other body tissues via the bloodstream and be utilized for the production of energy via the glycolytic cycle as already described.

β-Oxidation

The fatty acids liberated during lipolysis constitute the major source of energy for the tissues of the body. Catabolism of these products involves the stepwise degradation of the fatty acid molecule, two carbon atoms being split off the long fatty acid chain in each step in the form of the compound *acetyl co-enzyme A* (Fig. 10.5b). Each step comprises a series of reactions and is termed a *β-oxidation*[1] (Fig. 10.5a).

The reactions are as follows:

(a) an initial activation of the fatty acid molecule brought about by its combination with co-enzyme A to yield a fatty acid-co-enzyme A ester. The activation *requires one molecule of ATP* to supply the energy necessary for driving the reaction;

(b) a dehydrogenation in which the dehydrogenase responsible is linked to a respiratory chain through the second co-enzyme, FAD. In terms of what was said earlier in the chapter, *two molecules of ATP* are *produced* for every two atoms of hydrogen which are removed from the fatty acid;

(c) a hydration in which a molecule of water combines with the unsaturated fatty acid-co-enzyme A ester resulting from reaction (b);

(d) a second dehydrogenation, the dehydrogenase in this instance being linked to a respiratory chain through NAD. This de-hydrogenation *yields three molecules of ATP* for every two atoms of hydrogen removed from the hydroxy acid-co-enzyme A, resulting from reaction (c);

(e) splitting of the resulting keto acid-co-enzyme A ester between the α and β carbon atoms. This splitting of the molecule requires a further molecule of co-enzyme A, the products of the

---

[1] It was customary to denote the various carbon atoms present in a fatty acid chain by the letters of the Greek alphabet, commencing with the carbon atom closest to the terminal carboxyl group. Since this is the α-carbon atom, the second one after the carboxyl group is the β-carbon atom. The fatty acid s split oxidatively at this point, hence the term β-oxidation.

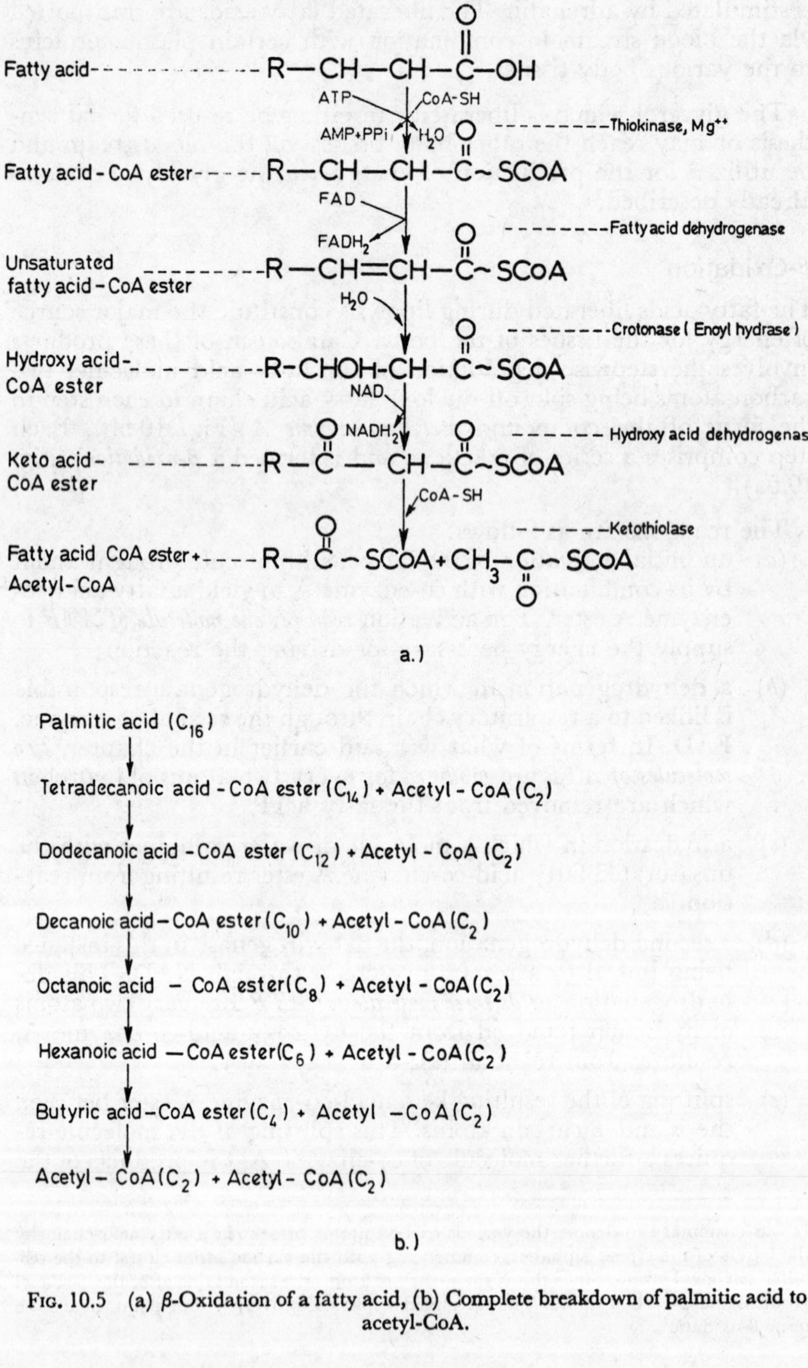

Fatty acid- - - - - - - - - - - - - - $R-CH-CH-\overset{\overset{O}{\parallel}}{C}-OH$

                  ATP

                  CoA-SH

             AMP+PPi H_2O - - - - - - - - -Thiokinase, Mg^{++}

Fatty acid - CoA ester - - - - - $R-CH-CH-\overset{\overset{O}{\parallel}}{C}\sim SCoA$

             FAD

             $FADH_2$ - - - - - - - -Fatty acid dehydrogenase

Unsaturated - - - - - - - - - - $R-CH=CH-\overset{\overset{O}{\parallel}}{C}\sim SCoA$
fatty acid - CoA ester

           H_2O

                   - - - - - - - -Crotonase (Enoyl hydrase)

Hydroxy acid - - - - - - - - - -$R-CHOH-CH-\overset{\overset{O}{\parallel}}{C}\sim SCoA$
CoA ester

            NAD

          $NADH_2$ - - - - - - Hydroxy acid dehydrogenase

Keto acid - - - - - - - - - -$R-\overset{\overset{O}{\parallel}}{C}-CH-\overset{\overset{O}{\parallel}}{C}\sim SCoA$
CoA ester

               CoA - SH

                   - - - - -Ketothiolase

Fatty acid CoA ester + - - - - $R-\overset{\overset{O}{\parallel}}{C}\sim SCoA + CH_3-\overset{\overset{O}{\parallel}}{C}\sim SCoA$
Acetyl- CoA

a.)

Palmitic acid (C_{16})

Tetradecanoic acid - CoA ester (C_{14}) + Acetyl - CoA (C_2)

Dodecanoic acid - CoA ester (C_{12}) + Acetyl - CoA (C_2)

Decanoic acid - CoA ester (C_{10}) + Acetyl - CoA (C_2)

Octanoic acid   - CoA ester (C_8) + Acetyl - CoA (C_2)

Hexanoic acid —CoA ester (C_6) + Acetyl - CoA (C_2)

Butyric acid –CoA ester (C_4) + Acetyl —CoA (C_2)

Acetyl – CoA (C_2) + Acetyl - CoA (C_2)

b.)

Fig. 10.5   (a) β-Oxidation of a fatty acid, (b) Complete breakdown of palmitic acid to acetyl-CoA.

reaction being the two carbon fragments, acetyl co-enzyme A and the co-enzyme A ester of the fatty acid residue which is now shorter by two carbon atoms. The process is repeated as often as is necessary to degrade the entire fatty acid chain into *acetyl co-enzyme A* fragments.

Each β-oxidation step yields *5 molecules of ATP*. A fatty acid like *palmitic acid* which contains sixteen carbon atoms undergoes seven β-oxidations before it is fully degraded to acetyl co-enzyme A. The *total* production of ATP is thus, *7 × 5 = 35 molecules*. Since one molecule was used for the initial activation of the fatty acid, the total yield is 34 molecules, a significantly greater yield of energy than the 8 molecules of ATP obtained from one molecule of glucose.

Furthermore the number of acetyl co-enzyme A molecules obtained from the catabolism of palmitic acid is seven, compared to the possible two from glycolysis. The acetyl co-enzyme A enters the common pathway of metabolism and during the transformation which it undergoes, the further production of a considerable amount of energy is possible.

If the fatty acid undergoing this stepwise oxidation is one with an uneven number of carbon atoms, the penultimate product in its complete degradation will be the compound, valeryl co-enzyme A (containing five carbon atoms) instead of butyryl co-enzyme A. Valeryl co-enzyme A is split, during the final β-oxidation, into one molecule of propionyl co-enzyme A (3 carbon atoms) and one molecule of acetyl co-enzyme A. Propionyl co-enzyme A is converted into succinyl co-enzyme A, and in this form can enter the common pathway of metabolism (see later).

The catabolism of proteins

The proteins present in many body tissues are in a continuous dynamic state of flux, that is, they are being continually formed and broken down and being re-formed again. There is thus a continuous interchange of amino acids between the tissue proteins and the tissue fluids. The amino acids present in the latter constitute the so-called amino acid pool. The proteins of the body tissue represent mainly enzymes and structural proteins and only relatively limited amounts are stored for the production of energy. Amino acids derived from protein catabolism, and amino acids derived from the diet, mix freely in the tissue fluid amino acid pool. Such amino acids can be used for the re-synthesis or *de novo* synthesis of proteins or they may be used for the production of energy. Any excess amino acids will generally be excreted via the urine. The blood level of these compounds is generally maintained relatively constant at 0,35 - 0,65g/l of blood, largely by active reabsorption in the kidney tubules and the transport maximum of the carrier systems.

Situations commonly arise in which the rate of utilization of amino acids for energy production is considerably enhanced. Such a situation is, for instance, fasting. The available liver glycogen stores probably last for no longer than about 6-8 hours in the average person and in order to maintain the blood sugar level, glucose must be produced from sources other than glycogen. A glance at the overall scheme of metabolism, depicted in Fig. 10.1 will show that pathways exist for the conversion of some amino acids to glucose, and it is in the form of glucose or other intermediate products that they can be used for the production of energy. The overall process is known as *gluconeogenesis*. Although in the strict sense the term means the *de novo* formation of glucose from amino acids, it is often used in a broader sense to indicate the increased catabolism of amino acids that occurs under certain circumstances.

The process is markedly stimulated by a group of hormones produced by the adrenal cortex, known collectively as the glucocorticoids, of which *cortisone* and *cortisol* are examples. These hormones are released when the body is placed in some sort of adverse circumstance, referred to in broad terms as *stress*. It may be a lowering of the environmental temperature, fasting, a mild disease state, fatigue or heightened emotional tension, to mention just a few everyday examples. One of the immediate responses of the body to stressful conditions is to raise the level of energy production in its tissues, by the secretion of the various hormones which stimulate a variety of catabolic processes, including amino acid catabolism.

A few basic mechanisms exist for handling all the amino acids whether they are derived from, or intended for, protein synthesis or whether they are obtained from the diet. The main purpose of these mechanisms is to accommodate the carbon atom skeletons of the amino acids, if possible into the major metabolic pathways which have already been discussed, or into the final common pathway of metabolism. In the catabolism of the amino acids, one of the main problems which exists is the removal of the nitrogen atom (in the form of the amino group) from the molecule, and its disposal. It is readily converted into ammonia, but since this is a toxic substance, it must be converted into a non-toxic and easily excreted substance, notably urea.

Transamination

The process, which represents a mechanism of major importance, is portrayed in Fig. 10.6a. In theory the amino group of an amino acid (compound 1 in the figure) can be exchanged for the oxygen atom

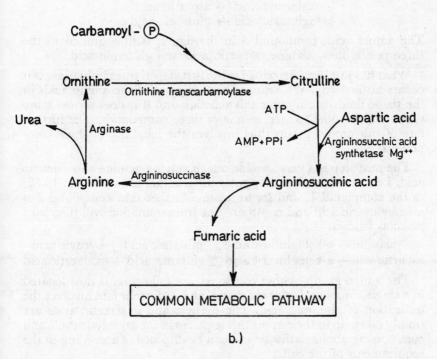

Fig. 10.6 (a) Transamination, (b) The urea cycle.

present in the ketone group of a keto acid (compound 2 in the figure). This exchange results in compound 1, the original amino acid, being converted into a keto acid, whilst compound two which accepts its amino group, becomes an amino acid (compound 3). If the keto acid which is formed (compound 4) is one which normally occurs as a metabolite in a metabolic pathway, e.g. *pyruvic acid, a-ketoglutaric acid, oxalacetic acid* or *aceto-acetic acid*, it can enter the pathway concerned and be used for energy production. If on the other hand it isn't, it may have to be transformed into one of these compounds. Such transformations exist for a number of amino acids. In a few instances, no mechanism exists for handling the keto acid and it is excreted in the urine.

Let us assume that the amino acid (compound 1) is any one of those found in proteins, and that compound 2 is only one of three keto acids, pyruvic acid, oxalacetic acid or α-ketoglutaric acid. If these accept an amino group in the exchange reaction explained above, the following will occur:

pyruvic acid → alanine
oxalacetic acid → aspartic acid
α-ketoglutaric acid → glutamic acid

The amino acid, compound 3 in the figure, is thus limited to the three possibilities, alanine, aspartic acid and glutamic acid.

What has just been described is the first step of transamination as it occurs in the body. We assumed that any one of the amino acids in the tissue fluids could enter this reaction and if it does so its amino group will become located in one of three compounds. The further fate of this amino group thus involves the handling of these compounds.

The next step is a very specific one, involving alanine and aspartic acid. Let us assume that they enter the reaction shown in Fig. 10.62, as the compound 1, and let us assume further that compound 2 is α-ketoglutaric acid and no other. The transamination will then take place as follows:

alanine + α-ketoglutaric acid ⇌ glutamic acid + pyruvic acid
aspartic acid + α-ketoglutaric acid ⇌ glutamic acid + oxalacetic acid

The amino group, whose course we are following, is now located in a single compound, glutamic acid, and its further fate involves the utilization of glutamic acid. The pyruvic and oxalacetic acids are simply taken up in their appropriate places in the glycolytic cycle and common metabolic pathway and can be disposed of according to the requirements of the cell.

Oxidative deamination

This type of reaction embraces the removal of the amino group from an amino acid, with the simultaneous oxidation of the carbon atom to which it was attached, thus leaving a keto acid as the main product of the reaction, as follows:

$$R\text{-}CHNH_2\text{-}COOH \xrightarrow{+O} R\text{-}CO\text{-}COOH + NH_3$$

Amino Acid   Keto Acid   Ammonia

Most of the amino acids can be handled in this way, but the mechanism does not appear to be of general importance in mammalian tissues, except for the deamination of glutamic acid.

In the case of *glutamic acid* the amino group in glutamic acid is oxidatively removed by the enzyme *glutamic dehydrogenase* as ammonia leaving α-ketoglutaric acid as the residue. The ammonia is at once taken up into the synthesis of urea (see later), while the α-ketoglutaric acid can enter some of the above reactions once more, or it can enter the common pathway of metabolism.

In the above transamination reactions the amino group is transferred from the amino acid to the keto acid acceptor by a transaminase. Enzymes of this type require pyridoxal phosphate (see chapters 8 and 12) as co-enzyme, this compound functioning as the actual carrier of the amino group. The transaminations involving aspartic acid and alanine are catalyzed by the specific enzymes *aspartate transaminase* (formerly known as glutamic-oxalacetic transaminase or GOT) and *alanine transaminase* (formerly known as glutamic-pyruvic transaminase or GPT). These enzymes occur in many tissues but large amounts of each are present in liver, skeletal muscle and heart muscle. When structures such as these suffer any acute destruction, large amounts of these enzymes leak from the damaged cells into the tissue fluids, and hence appear in high concentrations in the blood plasma. Use is made of this in clinical laboratory medicine, the elevated plasma levels of these enzymes being indicative of liver, myocardial or skeletal muscle damage.

The synthesis of urea

The events leading to the incorporation of the amino group removed from glutamic acid into the urea molecule are collectively known as the *urea cycle*. This is shown in schematic form in figure 10.6b. The following are the main events in this cycle:

(a) the amino group stripped off glutamic acid is combined with carbon dioxide in the presence of ATP to form carbamoyl phosphate;

(b) the carbamoyl phosphate is combined with ornithine to form citrulline, which in turn is combined with aspartic acid (produced in transamination reactions such as described above) to form argininosuccinic acid;

(c) this compound is split yielding arginine and fumaric acid. The fumaric acid enters the common pathway of metabolism and can be reconverted to aspartic acid via this pathway and transamination of pyruvic acid. This particular mechanism permits the direct disposal of some of the amino groups in the

form of aspartic acid, instead of all the amino groups having
to go through the glutamic acid steps mentioned above.

(d) The arginine formed can be split into urea and ornithine.
The urea which is formed passes into the tissue fluids and then
into the blood to be excreted by the kidneys. In this way the
amino group nitrogen is disposed of in a safe and efficient

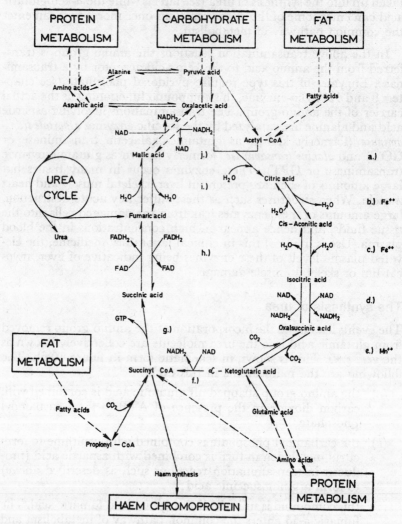

FIG. 10.7 The common metabolic pathway (Krebs cycle, tricarboxylic acid cycle)
(Enzymes: (a) citrate synthetase, (b) and (c) aconitase, (d) isocitric acid dehydrogenase,
(e) oxal-succinic acid decarboxylase, (f) keto-glutaric acid dehydrogenase, (g) succinate
thiokinase, (h) succinic dehydrogenase, (i) fumarase, (j) malic acid dehydrogenase.)

manner. Arginine can, however, be put to some important uses. It can be used for the synthesis of the protein part of the nucleoprotein molecule. Together with the amino acid glycine, it is used for the synthesis of creatine phosphate. It is likely that appreciable amounts of arginine are diverted into these synthetic pathways.

The ornithine which is formed in this step can re-enter the urea cycle, but appreciable quantities of it appear to be diverted into the synthesis of the amino acid proline and hence proteins like collagen, as well as into the synthesis of biologically important compounds like spermine and spermidine. These compounds have an important but poorly understood role in the growth and division of cells.

The common pathway of metabolism

The end point of the metabolic transformations in the glycolytic cycle is pyruvic acid; that of the stepwise β-oxidation of fatty acids, acetyl co-enzyme A; and of the degradation of amino acids by transamination, the keto acids, pyruvic, oxalacetic and α-ketoglutaric acid. These products are fed into a common metabolic pathway known also as the *tricarboxylic acid cycle* or *Krebs cycle*. This pathway is presented schematically in Fig. 10.7. The reactions involved take place largely in the mitochondria, and serve the following purposes:

(a) They link the major metabolic cycles to one another as shown in Fig. 10.1, and permit the ready interconversion of one type of nutrient into another;

(b) there are four dehydrogenation steps in the cycle, each of which is coupled to a respiratory chain and yields three high energy phosphate compounds like ATP and GTP for every two hydrogen atoms oxidized. Thus for every molecule of acetyl co-enzyme A which enters the cycle and goes through all the transformations, the energy yield in terms of ATP only is a possible twelve molecules of ATP;

(c) the cycle is the centre for the production of a number of important chemical substances, e.g. α-ketoglutaric acid for transamination reactions and the synthesis of amino acids, succinyl co-enzyme A for the synthesis of haem and thus of haemoglobin and oxalacetic acid for the synthesis of aspartic acid and thus of urea;

(d) amino acids in which the carbon skeletons are capable of transformation to α-ketoglutaric acid, succinyl co-enzyme A oxalacetic acid and pyruvic acid, can enter the cycle and can, by means of the transformation shown in Fig. 10.3, be converted to glucose. These are the basic transformations underlying gluconeogenesis;

(e) carbon dioxide is produced in the steps involving the conversion of pyruvic acid to acetyl co-enzyme A and α-ketoglutaric acid to succinyl co-enzyme A (see chapter 11 regarding carbon dioxide).

We need also to take note of the following points of interest regarding this cycle:

(i) Although the reactions which make up this pathway are presented in the form of a cycle, it does not necessarily follow that acetyl co-enzyme A entering the cycle undergoes all the metabolic transformations leading to the formation of oxalacetic acid. Considerable amounts of acetyl co-enzyme A are diverted via α-ketoglutaric acid into glutamic acid and amino acid synthesis. A significant diversion occurs via succinyl co-enzyme into the synthesis of haem. The yield of ATP mentioned earlier is thus only a potential one.

(ii) The reactions involved in the cycle are reversible except for the steps, α-ketoglutaric acid to succinic acid. The irreversible steps facilitate the diversions mentioned, as well as the gluconeogenetic transformations mentioned earlier.

(iii) Acetyl co-enzyme A, formed by the stepwise β-oxidation of fatty acids and from pyruvic acid, can only enter the common pathway if there is sufficient oxalacetic acid present for it to combine with. Although oxalacetic acid is being continually generated in the cycle, a large amount of it is diverted into transamination reactions and the synthesis of aspartic acid. The major source of oxalacetic acid is glucose, it being formed from pyruvic acid produced during glycolysis. For this very reason, an adequate supply of carbohydrates in our diet is essential.

The production of energy from nutrient substances

The heat produced by the combustion of the major nutrients in the tissues of our body is in the following order:

carbohydrates	17kJ/g
proteins	17kJ/g
fats	38kJ/g

If the composition of our daily diet is known in terms of carbohydrates, proteins and fats, we can calculate the daily intake of potential energy. It is obvious from these figures that fats yield far more energy than do carbohydrates or proteins. The figures cited above are obtained when the major nutrients are burnt under experimental conditions in an atmosphere of oxygen. The actual energy yield in the body is somewhat greater, since foodstuffs in general exert a stimulating effect on metabolism known as the *specific dynamic action* of nutrient substances. Carbohydrates, proteins and fats yield respectively approximately 5, 30 and 5 per cent. more energy when they are metabolized than the theoretical values presented above. The energy increment is due for instance to the breakdown of ATP at various stages to provide energy for the active transport of nutrients and for the activation of these before they enter the metabolic cycles.

It is possible to assess the energy yield from compounds like glucose or fatty acids in terms of ATP as follows: The oxidation of one molecule of glucose in the presence of sufficient oxygen can yield 8 molecules of ATP, to the step where two molecules of pyruvic acid are produced. Although we have not studied it, we may note that the conversion of these two molecules to two molecules of acetyl co-enzyme A is accompanied by the formation of two further molecules of ATP. If both of these two molecules of acetyl co-enzyme A were to pass through all the transformations of the common pathway of metabolism to yield oxalacetic acid, the further yield of energy would be in terms of ATP, 24 molecules. The total amount of ATP that could be harvested from the complete catabolism of glucose could theoretically be 34 molecules.

The degradation of one molecule of palmitic acid to acetyl co-enzyme A by stepwise β-oxidation, yields 34 molecules of ATP and 8 molecules of acetyl co-enzyme A. If each of these molecules of acetyl co-enzyme A were to pass through all the transformations of the common pathway of metabolism, the energy yield in terms of ATP would be 96 molecules. The total theoretical yield of ATP would be 130 molecules. This is about four times the yield obtained from one molecule of glucose.

Although not specifically mentioned, the catabolism of amino acids whose carbon skeletons can be so transformed that they can enter a metabolic pathway, is generally accompanied by at least one dehydrogenation step. For each molecule of an amino acid used for energy production, at least three molecules of ATP can be formed. The theoretical total yield is greater and depends at what point the carbon skeleton enters a particular pathway.

The rate at which metabolic phenomena proceed is generally held constant at a certain level, and is best appreciated when an inividdual is completely at rest. We term this rate the *basal metabolic rate* (BMR). This is a measurable quantity and is generally expressed as kilojoules per square metre of body surface per hour ($kJ/m^2/h$). It is defined as the lowest level of energy at which cells can still function normally and so maintain life. In a person maintaining a constant BMR the rate of catabolism is equal to the rate of anabolism and the body mass should remain constant. The BMR thus remains constant in any healthy individual but varies from person to person according to age, sex, body size, race and the environment in which a person lives.

In general, the BMR is low in the new-born, but gradually increases to reach a maximum at about five years of age, after which it gradually declines once more. At the age of six years the BMR is for example, about 270-222kJ/m^2/h, while at the age of twenty-one years it lies in the range 151-172kJ/m^2/h. It is lower in women than in men and is lower in persons living in hot climates than in those who live in more temperate regions. In general, persons of small build have a higher BMR per unit of body surface than larger individuals.

The BMR is generally determined by measuring the oxygen consumption in a person at complete rest. The person should have fasted for at least twelve hours and during the actual measurements, should be recumbent, completely relaxed and awake. Measurements are generally made at a room temperature of 20-25°C.

The metabolic rate increases during activity and in hard exercise may be in the order of six to eight times the basal rate. The daily energy requirements of each individual vary thus according to the physical activity of the person. The energy requirements of the average 70kg person are for instance —

> 272 kJ/hour during sleep;
> 418 kJ/hour whilst sitting at rest;
> 836 kJ/hour during slow walking;
> 2 383 kJ/hour during running; and
> about 4 600 kJ/hour whilst climbing stairs.

Carbohydrate anabolism

Glucose and the related monosaccharides can be used for a number of synthetic purposes, for instance *glycogenesis* (the synthesis of glycogen in liver and muscles), the synthesis of complex polysaccharides which are part of cell membranes or which perform other physiological functions, the synthesis of disaccharides like lactose in the lactating mammary gland and so on.

The majority of the reactions in the glycolytic cycle are fully reversible in the majority of the body tissues (Fig. 10.3). The reversibility of the final step, i.e. that ·between phospho-enol pyruvic acid and pyruvic acid poses certain problems, which need not concern us at the moment. A by-pass of this step exists by which oxalacetic acid formed in the common pathway or from pyruvic acid can be converted directly into phospho-enol pyruvic acid. This greatly facilitates the process of *gluconeogenesis*. Whilst we have used this term to cover mainly the conversion of certain amino acids to glucose, it also covers the conversion of compounds like lactic acid and glycerol to glucose. Gluconeogenesis proceeds generally by a reversal of the reactions in the glycolytic cycle, from phospho-enol pyruvic acid upwards. The process of gluconeogenesis occurs mainly in the liver and, as we have seen, is stimulated by the *glucocorticoid hormones, cortisol* and *cortisone.*

As explained earlier gluconeogenesis occurs when the liver glycogen reserves become depleted or when the body is placed in any stressful circumstances. Gluconeogenesis leads to the formation of glucose-6-phosphate which can be converted to glucose for maintaining the blood sugar level through the activity of the enzyme glucose-6-phosphatase. Alternately it may be converted into glycogen by the process of *glycogenesis.* The latter process involves the conversion of glucose-6-phosphate to glucose-1-phosphate and this, by a rather complex mechanism, to glycogen.

Fat anabolism

This involves the synthesis of fatty acids, the synthesis of stored triglycerides and the synthesis of complex lipids, like phospholipids and lipoproteins, which form part of cell membranes.

Fatty acid synthesis

The process is a complex one, part of which occurs in the mitochondria of cells and part of which occurs in the cytoplasm. The starting materials are acetyl co-enzyme A, derived either from pyruvic acid or from fatty acid catabolism, and carbon dioxide and hydrogen ions, both of which are largely derived from reactions in the pentose monophosphate shunt. The process requires the vitamins, biotin and pantothenic acid, both of which form part of carrier molecules. The biotin-containing co-enzyme functions as a carbon dioxide carrier, while the pantothenic acid is part of a molecule carrying fatty acid residues during the synthesis. After the initial combination of acetyl co-enzyme A and carbon dioxide, the reactions concerned are essentially the reverse of those illustrated for the process of β-oxidation in Fig. 10.5a. With each set of these reactions, a saturated fatty acid containing an even number of carbon atoms in its chain is produced. Lengthening of the chain occurs through the addition of further carbon dioxide and acetyl co-enzyme A to the molecule and the reactions shown in Fig. 10.5a are repeated once more. The whole process is repeated until palmitic acid with sixteen carbon atoms is formed. The events described take place on the endoplasmic reticulum of cells. The synthesis of the eighteen carbon compound, stearic acid, requires some additional manipulations. The palmitic acid which is formed is transported into the mitochondria in combination with a carrier molecule known as *carnitine*. Pyridoxal phosphate and co-enzyme A are essential co-enzymes in the final steps of the synthesis. Manganese ions (Mn^{++}) are also essential for the synthesis of fatty acids.

Lipogenesis

This is the formation of triglycerides (or neutral fats) from glycerol and fatty acids. The fatty acids are initially activated by combination with co-enzyme A and the glycerol by phosphorylation. Synthesis of triglycerides occurs then according to the equation

3 fatty acid-co-enzyme A ester + glycerol phosphate = triglyceride + Pi + 3 co-enzyme A

Both the acetyl co-enzyme required for the synthesis of fatty acids and the glycerol can be derived from carbohydrate metabolism. A significant part of our daily carbohydrate intake appears to be converted directly into fat. The process of lipogenesis, which occurs in the liver, adipose tissue and the mammary tissue, is stimulated by the hormone *insulin*.

Protein anabolism

This involves the synthesis of amino acids and protein synthesis. The proteins being formed in the body include the structural components of cell membranes, enzymes, plasma proteins and stored proteins.

Amino acid synthesis

Earlier in the chapter, we noted the fact that when the amino acids present in the amino acid pool were utilized in the transamination mechanisms described, there were some amino acids that could be so transformed that their carbon atom skeletons could enter the major metabolic pathways. These reactions are reversible and the amino acids concerned can thus be formed from the particular metabolites representing their point of entry into these pathways. We noted the fact, however, that there were also some amino acids whose carbon skeletons could not be transformed into compounds which occur in the major pathways. No pathways therefore exist for the synthesis of such amino acids in mammalian tissues. In a few instances some of the reactions mentioned immediately above are not truly reversible in mammalian cells. Amino acids which are not synthesized in mammalian cells must be obtained from the diet. Such amino acids are referred to as *essential amino acids* and include *histidine, leucine, isoleucine, lysine, methionine, phenylalanine, threonine, tryptophane* and *valine*.

Protein synthesis

This topic has been dealt with at length in chapter 8. The student will do well to refresh his memory of the process at this point. The process which takes place on the ribosomes, includes the activation of amino acids, the incorporation of these in the correct sequence into the polypeptide chains, which are in the process of formation, and the final arrangement of these chains to form the protein molecule.

CHAPTER 11

The handling of end-products of metabolism by the body

The end products of metabolism can be arranged in three definite groups according to how the body handles them:

(i) substances which are generally fully utilized by the body, but which at any given moment may be present in tissue fluids in excess of the needs of the body, e.g. pyruvic acid, lactic acid, aceto-acetic acid, etc.;

(ii) substances normally used by the body, but whose concentration in the blood and tissue fluids must be maintained within certain narrow limits and be continually adjusted to fit changing circumstances, e.g. carbon dioxide in the form of bicarbonate ions, hydrogen ions, water, electrolytes and minerals;

(iii) substances which are true waste products and whose elimination is desirable, e.g. ammonium ions, urea, uric acid, creatinine and bilirubin.

For many of the substances in the first two groups, active reabsorption mechanisms are known to exist and to govern their rate of reabsorption from the kidney tubules. As explained earlier in this book, the rate of reabsorption by such systems is adjusted to the desirable concentrations at which the substances concerned occur in blood and tissue fluids. Anything in excess of these will be eliminated in the urine. Considerations such as this are particularly relevant to the substances in the second group. Water, electrolytes and the minerals of importance have been fully dealt with in the preceding chapters; some facts of importance still remain to be considered regarding carbon dioxide, bicarbonate ions and hydrogen ions.

The organs of excretion are the kidneys, lungs, skin and intestines. With regard to the latter, we can note in passing that a number of drugs are excreted in the saliva, and that various drugs and waste products are excreted in the bile. Some substances are excreted directly through the walls of the intestine. All these products are eliminated via the faeces. Small amounts of waste products and some drugs are excreted in the sweat, whilst some toxic minerals like arsenic and copper are deposited in the growing hair and are in effect placed outside the tissues of the body. Our main concern in the present chapter is, however, the elimination of waste products via the lungs and the kidneys.

The physiological importance of carbon dioxide

Allusion was made earlier to some of the uses of carbon dioxide in the body. These must now be considered in some detail. Carbon dioxide is important in:

(a) *The regulation of respiration.* Certain discrete areas in the brain, notably in the medulla oblongata and the pons, known as the respiratory centres, are sensitive to the concentration of carbon dioxide in the blood. A rise in the carbon dioxide content of the blood stimulates the despatch from these centres of a stream of nerve impulses which initiate faster and deeper respiration.

(b) *The central regulation of circulation.* The centre in the brain controlling the heart rate and the vasomoter centre in the medulla controlling the bore of the arterioles throughout the body, are sensitive to the carbon dioxide content of blood. A rise in this causes an increased heart rate and vasoconstriction and hence improved blood pressure.

(c) *The local regulation of circulation.* Passage of carbon dioxide from the tissues into the capillary blood results in local increases of the levels of this gas in the blood perfusing the tissues. This causes local vasodilatation, thus increasing the blood flow in the tissues concerned. This is particularly important with regard to the cerebral circulation.

(d) *The regulation of the acid-base balance.* Carbon dioxide reacts with water, forming carbonic acid. This weak acid dissociates yielding hydrogen and bicarbonate ions. Carbonic acid and the liberated bicarbonate ions constitute an important buffer pair, which will be discussed later in this chapter.

(e) *The synthesis of a variety of useful chemicals.* Carbon dioxide is combined with ammonia in the presence of ATP to form carbamoyl phosphate. This very important compound is used for the synthesis of arginine, urea and pyrimidines. As pointed out earlier, arginine is required amongst other things for the synthesis of the protein moeity of nucleoproteins. Pyrimidines are an integral part of the nucleic acid moeity of these compounds. In this respect carbon dioxide is of vital importance.

Carbon dioxide is used for the synthesis of fatty acids as explained in the previous chapter. It is used for the conversion of pyruvic acid to oxalacetic acid and for the conversion of propionyl co-enzyme A to succinyl co-enzyme A. In reactions such as these it is bound to a biotin-containing co-enzyme. It is used for the production of hydrochloric acid in the stomach (chapter 9).

The inter-relationship of hydrogen ions and carbon dioxide

Carbon dioxide combines with water to form carbonic acid:

$$CO_2 + H_2O \rightleftharpoons H_2CO_3 \qquad \cdots \cdots \cdots \quad (1)$$

The reaction is speeded up enormously by the enzyme *carbonic anhydrase*, which is present, for instance, in the erythrocytes, kidney tubule cells and the oxcyntic cells of the stomach. In such sites, high levels of carbonic acid can be accumulated rapidly. Carbonic acid is a weak acid, dissociating poorly as follows:

$$H_2CO_3 \rightleftharpoons H^+ + HCO_3^- \qquad \cdots \cdots \cdots \quad (2)$$

Small amounts of carbon dioxide also pass into solution in water without combining chemically with it. A solution of carbon dioxide will thus contain at any given moment,

$$CO_2, \ H_2O, \ H_2CO_3, \ H^+ \text{ and } HCO_3^-$$

According to the principles explained in chapter 5, the mixture will be an equilibrium mixture in which the relative concentrations of the five substances will remain constant at a given temperature and pressure. A change in the concentration of any one of these substances, induced by adding more of, or removing some of, the substance concerned, will induce a change in the state of equilibrium of the mixture. The addition of more carbon dioxide to the system will shift the equilibrium of reaction (1) to the right, removal of hydrogen ions will shift the equilibrium of reaction (2) to the right, while the addition of bicarbonate ions will shift the equilibrium of reaction (2) to the left, and so on. Considerations such as these are of great importance in the handling of both hydrogen ions and carbon dioxide in the body, as will be seen shortly.

Since sodium and potassium ions are abundant in the blood and tissue fluids, the following reactions take place readily:

$$K^+ + HCO_3^- \rightleftharpoons KHCO_3 \qquad \cdots \cdots \cdots \quad (3)$$
$$\text{and, } Na^+ + HCO_3^- \rightleftharpoons NaHCO_3 \qquad \cdots \cdots \cdots \quad (4)$$

Reaction (3) takes place to a large extent within cells, since most of the potassium in the body is located intracellularly. Reaction (4) is typical of the extracellular fluids where most of the sodium in the body is located.

The transport of carbon dioxide in the blood

Carbon dioxide is transported in the blood in three ways:

(i) *In solution.* When carbon dioxide diffuses out of the tissues in which it is produced, it does so in solution in the tissue fluids. The amount which dissolves is dependant on the local carbon dioxide pressure. Once in solution it exerts a pressure which is proportional to its concentration in the solution. The tissue fluids do in fact contain a mixture of gases in solution, notably oxygen, carbon dioxide and nitrogen. Each of these gases in the mixture exerts a pressure which is proportional to the concentration of the particular gas and independent of the concentration of the others. We refer to it as the *partial pressure* of the gas, since the pressure exerted by gas mixture as a whole is the sum of the individual gas pressures. We designate the partial pressure of gases by symbols as follows: Po_2, Pco_2, etc. The partial pressure of carbon dioxide (Pco_2) in solution determines the amount of carbon dioxide which can diffuse from the tissues into the blood plasma, and from the blood plasma into the red blood cells; it also determines how much will react with water and how much will diffuse from the blood plasma into the alveoli of the lungs. About 5-7 per cent of the carbon dioxide carried in blood is present in solution.

(ii) *In combination with haemoglobin.* Like all proteins the haemoglobin molecule contains free carboxyl and amino groups. At the pH of the fluid within the erythrocytes the free amino groups of haemoglobin can bind with carbon dioxide to form *carbamino-haemoglobin.* This generally occurs at high partial pressures of carbon dioxide. When the Pco_2 is low, carbamino haemoglobin readily decomposes, yielding up the carbon dioxide carried in this way. About 10 per cent of the carbon dioxide transported in blood is carried in this manner.

(iii) *In the form of the bicarbonate ion.* About 60-90 per cent of the carbon dioxide carried in blood is transported in this way. As the Pco_2 in the plasma rises, so carbon dioxide diffuses into the red blood cells and combines rapidly with some of the intracellular water, in the presence of carbonic anhydrase, forming carbonic acid (reaction 1) above. This dissociates yielding bicarbonate and hydrogen ions (reaction 2). The hydrogen ions are taken up by the haemoglobin in the erythrocytes, which like all proteins has buffering ability, while the bicarbonate ions associate with intracellular potassium ions to form potassium bicarbonate (reaction 3 above). When the bicarbonate content of the cells reaches a certain level, these ions start diffusing out of the erythrocytes into the plasma. In order to maintain the ionic balance in the blood, some of the chloride ions diffuse simultaneously into the red blood cells. The bicarbonate ions in the plasma associate with sodium ions, forming sodium bicarbonate, the form in which most of the carbon dioxide is carried. The exchange of chloride for bicarbonate ions which occurs during the transport of carbon dioxide is known as the *chloride shift* or *Hamburger phenomenon.*

The excretion of carbon dioxide by the lungs

The partial pressure of carbon dioxide in the alveoli of the lungs is lower than that in the venous blood arriving at the lungs:

$$P_{CO_2} \text{ (lungs)} \qquad = 40mm \, Hg$$
$$P_{CO_2} \text{ (venous blood)} = 46mm \, Hg$$

This favours the movement of carbon dioxide from the venous blood into the alveoli. As carbon dioxide leaves the plasma, so it changes the whole equilibrium of the transport mixture. Carbamino-haemoglobin readily decomposes, giving up its carbon dioxide to the plasma. The equilibrium of reactions (2) and (1) above is shifted to the left, leading to the production of carbon dioxide and water. The carbon dioxide which is released then diffuses rapidly out into the alveoli of the lungs as before.

The excretion of other substances by the lungs

Apart from carbon dioxide, the lungs are capable of excreting a wide variety of volatile products formed during metabolism or which are absorbed from the ingested food in the digestive tract; for instance, acetone, an abnormal metabolite formed in the tissues of diabetics, or the odiferous principles in garlic, or alcohol, and other volatile principles present in liquor. About 500ml of water in the form of vapour is excreted by the lungs each day. This insensible loss of water is of importance in the whole problem of maintaining the water balance in the body, as explained earlier in this book.

The regulation of the hydrogen ion concentration in the body

It should be apparent from the material in the foregoing chapters that the hydrogen ion is a most reactive substance. It is imperative therefore that the hydrogen ion concentration of body fluids be maintained constant within very narrow limits, that is, between the pH values of 7,3-7,4. Since acids yield up hydrogen ions to solutions they tend to lower the pH, by increasing the hydrogen ion concentrations. Alkalis conversely tend to raise the pH value as explained in chapter 5. In the same chapter we encountered the phenomenon of *"buffer action"* and noted that a buffer pair consisted of a weak acid and a salt of that acid, or a weak alkali and a salt of that alkali.

There are various ways in which the body can neutralise the effects of acidic or alkaline substances which enter the blood and tissue fluids, and maintain a constant hydrogen ion concentration, for instance

(i) by the buffer action of compounds present within these fluids or within the cells of the tissues of the body;

(ii) by the excretion of hydrogen ions in the urine, usually in the form of the ammonium ion or acidic ions such as the dihydrogen phosphate ion $(H_2PO_4^-)$;

(iii) by the increased excretion of carbon dioxide through the lungs, or of the bicarbonate ion through the kidneys.

Buffer systems

(i) *The proteins present in the cells and fluids of the body.* Proteins are amphoteric substances, that is, substances which are capable of acting either as acids or as bases, depending upon the pH of their environment. They are able to do so since their molecules contain both free acidic carboxyl groups and free amino groups, which have alkaline properties. When placed in an acidic medium these amino groups ionise and attract hydrogen ions, thus decreasing the hydrogen ion concentration. If the environment is an alkaline one the carboxyl groups ionise, contributing hydrogen ions to the medium, and attracting positively charged ions like sodium or potassium ions. It will be remembered that hydrogen ions released in such alkaline circumstances combine with hydroxyl ions to form the poorly dissociated water molecule as follows:

$$H^+ + OH^- \rightleftharpoons H_2O$$

The proteins of importance in this respect are the plasma proteins, the haemoglobin in the erythrocytes and many protein molecules located within the tissue cells.

Although proteins are excellent buffers, their buffering capacity in the tissue fluids is somewhat limited by the relatively small number of protein molecules present. Although the concentration of proteins in the plasma is for instance considerably higher than that of bicarbonate or phosphate ions, the very high molecular masses of these proteins simply means that fewer particles of protein will be present in the plasma than is the case with the very small ions mentioned.

(ii) *The bicarbonate buffer system.* The buffer pair concerned is carbonic acid and sodium bicarbonate. The attention of the student is focused on the discussion of buffer action, presented in chapter 5, where this buffer pair is used as a pertinent example to explain buffer action. Both members of the pair dissociate poorly. Addition of acid to the system containing them leads to the formation of more poorly dissociated carbonic acid; addition of alkali simply results in the formation of more of the poorly dissociated bicarbonate salt of the particular alkali added. In the first instance the excess carbonic acid which is produced disturbs the equilibrium mentioned earlier in the chapter. The result is an increased output of carbon dioxide from the lungs. The excess of bicarbonate ions formed in the second instance is handled in the following way. The bicarbonate ions associate in the plasma or tissue fluids with sodium ions and are conveyed to the kidneys in the form of sodium bicarbonate. The sodium ions are exchanged in the kidney tubules for ammonium ions, produced specifically for this purpose. The sodium is reabsorbed and the excess bicarbonate passes into the urine as ammonium bicarbonate.

(iii) *The phosphate buffer system.* The buffer pair in this instance is the dihydrogen phosphate ($H_2PO_4^-$ which is the acidic component) and the monohydrogen phosphate ion ($HPO_4^=$, the salt component). Both are present in the blood and tissue fluids in association with sodium or potassium ions (e.g. as NaH_2PO_4 and Na_2HPO_4).

The buffer pair functions in the following way. If an acid, for instance hydrochloric acid, is added to such a system, the following reactions will occur:

$$HCl \rightleftharpoons H^+ + Cl^-$$
$$Na_2HPO_4 \rightleftharpoons 2Na^+ + HPO_4^=$$
$$Na^+ + H^+ + HPO_4^- \rightleftharpoons NaH_2PO_4$$
$$Na^+ + Cl^- \rightleftharpoons NaCl$$

The poorly dissociated acidic salt NaH_2PO_4 and sodium chloride are formed, with little resulting change in the pH of the medium. Addition of an alkali like sodium hydroxide to the system, will bring about the following reactions:

$$NaOH \rightleftharpoons Na^+ + OH^-$$
$$NaH_2PO_4 \rightleftharpoons Na^+ + H_2PO_4^-$$
$$H_2PO_4^- \rightleftharpoons H^+ + HPO_4^=$$
$$H^+ + OH^- \rightleftharpoons H_2O$$
$$2Na^+ + HPO_4^= \rightleftharpoons Na_2HPO_4$$

Poorly dissociated Na_2HPO_4 and water are formed with little resulting alteration in pH.

Although hydrochloric acid and sodium hydroxide never find their way into tissue fluids under normal circumstances, the general principles represented by the equations above, apply to the handling of acidic or alkaline waste substances normally present in tissue fluids. Excess hydrogen ions are conveyed to the kidneys in the form of NaH_2PO_4. The sodium can be exchanged for the ammonium ion, as in the case of excess bicarbonate, and the excess hydrogen ions are excreted as $NH_4H_2PO_4$ (ammonium dihydrogen phosphate). Excess sodium ions can be excreted as Na_2HPO_4 (disodium monohydrogen phosphate) by the kidneys. The phosphate ion in this case, can if necessary be exchanged for a bicarbonate ion, which is readily produced in the tubule cells of the kidney by the activity of carbonic anhydrase.

The secretion of hydrogen ions and the formation of ammonium ions by the kidneys

The tubule cells of the kidneys are able to secrete hydrogen ions directly into the filtrate present in the tubules. At the same time they are capable of forming and excreting ammonia in the same manner. The formation of ammonia occurs by means of the following important reaction, catalysed by the enzyme *glutaminase*:

$$\text{Glutamine} \rightleftharpoons \text{Glutamic acid} + NH_3$$

The ammonia which is formed immediately associates with the secreted hydrogen ions in the filtrate present in the tubules as follows:

$$H^+ + NH_3 \rightarrow NH_4^+$$

The ammonium ion which is formed, is in itself a means of eliminating excess hydrogen ions, but as we have just seen, it is also used to conserve sodium ions, by means of the exchange reactions mentioned. It then associates with negative ions such as HCO_3^-, $H_2PO_4^-$ or the chloride ion, and is excreted in this form in the urine.

Respiratory alkalosis and acidosis

The bicarbonate buffer system is the most important system of this nature present in the blood plasma. Variations in the carbon dioxide content of the blood can thus affect the composition of this system significantly, and these effects will be reflected in small changes in the pH of the plasma. Such changes, although small in terms of pH units, involve large changes in the hydrogen ion concentration and may have profound consequences. Symptoms of an acidosis appear when the pH of plasma falls below 7,3, and those of an alkalosis when it rises above 7,4.

Very rapid breathing (hyperventilation) causes an excessive loss of carbon dioxide from the blood. The concentration of hydrogen ions present is reduced and the condition which develops is known as a *respiratory alkalosis*. If on the other hand normal gas exchange in the lungs is impaired, e.g. through pneumonia, carbon dioxide accumulates in the blood, the concentration of hydrogen ions present is increased and a *respiratory acidosis* makes its appearance.

Metabolic alkalosis and acidosis

A *metabolic alkalosis* makes its appearance when large amounts of acid are lost from the body, as in prolonged vomiting. Although not strictly metabolic in origin, the term is sometimes used to denote the alkalosis occasioned by the ingestion of excessive amounts of alkaline salts like sodium bicarbonate.

A *metabolic acidosis* is generally seen when acidic substances are produced in one or other of the metabolic pathways at a rate faster than they can be cleared by the activities of the common pathway of metabolism or be excreted by the kidneys. Such acidic substances include lactic acid which may accumulate in the tissues during hard exercise. Aceto-acetic acid and related compounds accumulate in the blood of untreated cases of diabetes. We have noted that the essential defect in *diabetes mellitus* is a failure to produce sufficient insulin. This results in a failure on the part of glucose to cross the membranes of insulin-dependant tissues, e.g. the skeletal muscles. We have also noted that glucose is the major source of oxalacetic acid for the common pathway of metabolism. The entry of acetyl co-enzyme A into this pathway is dependant on the constant availability of oxalacetic acid. In untreated *diabetes mellitus* lipolysis is considerably accelerated to meet the demands occasioned by the failure of many tissues to utilize glucose. Since there will also be a failure to produce adequate amounts of oxalacetic acid, acetyl co-enzyme A accumulates in the tissues, much of it being converted to aceto-acetic acid and related acidic compounds. The result is the metabolic acidosis typical of diabetes mellitus, with its attendant depression of nerve function, and in severe cases coma and death.

Again, although not strictly metabolic in origin, the term is applied to the acidosis which may develop during a prolonged diarrhoea. In cases such as this the bicarbonate which is normally secreted in the bile and pancreatic juice is not reabsorbed, but lost from the body in excessive amounts, again causing shifts in the carbonic acid-bicarbonate-carbon dioxide equilibrium mentioned earlier, towards the acid side.

General excretory functions of the kidneys

The kidneys are the main organs of excretion in the body, removing waste substances, potentially harmful substances and the excess of nutrient substances from the bloodstream. The kidneys receive a very large share of the circulating blood. About 20-25 per cent of the blood in circulation passes through the kidneys at any given moment. In more practical terms the blood flow through the kidneys is 1,2 litres per minute. The excretory function of the kidneys depends largely on three phenomena; *filtration* which takes place at the glomerulus of each nephron, and *reabsorption* and *secretion* which takes place in the tubular parts of the nephrons. Filtration and reabsorption have been discussed at length in chapter 5; the secretion of hydrogen ions and ammonia have been mentioned earlier in this chapter.

We often adopt the following classification of substances which are filtered at the glomerulus; the classification being based upon whether the substances are reabsorbed in the tubules or not, and if they are, to what degree this occurs.

1. *High threshold substances.* These are essential nutrients, which are reabsorbed by active transport mechanisms. For each one of these a transport maximum exists, which is determined by the desired concentration in the blood of the substance concerned. This matter is also discussed at length in chapter 5. The attention of the student is drawn to that particular discussion. Substances of this type include sodium ions, glucose, and amino acids.

2. *Medium threshold substances.* The reabsorption of these compounds depends on events taking place in the kidney tubules, and instead of being actively reabsorbed they may even be actively secreted. Examples of substances of this type are hydrogen, potassium and ammonium ions.

3. *Low threshold substances* are generally true waste products, and are in most instances scarcely reabsorbed at all. Such substances include urea, uric acid, creatinine, dihydrogen-phosphate ions ($H_2PO_4^-$) and sulphate ions. Creatinine is secreted by the tubule cells into the glomerular filtrate.

The usual yellow colour of urine is due to the pigment *urochrome*. The origin of this pigment is unclear, but it is believed to derive from protein catabolism. At times coloured substances present in the diet can tint the urine. The red pigment of beetroot can colour the urine of certain individuals quite distinctly. The odour of urine is normally not unpleasant. Unpleasant odours can often be imparted to it by substances absorbed from the diet, e.g. the odiferous principles present in asparagus.

The excretory functions of the skin

The main excretory structures in the skin are the sweat glands. Sweat is a watery secretion containing amongst other things sodium chloride and small amounts of waste products such as urea, lactic and potassium ions. Certain drugs are also excreted in small amounts in the sweat.

The excretion of water in the form of sweat is intimately concerned with the process of the *regulation of body temperature*. When a fluid, such as sweat, evaporates, it draws heat from its surroundings to enable it to do so. In this instance the heat concerned is heat produced within the body, and sweating thus promotes the reduction of body heat.

Sodium chloride excretion via the sweat is variable and regulated to suit the needs of the body with respect to sodium. A high salt intake can affect, for instance, a threefold increase in the sodium chloride excretion via the sweat. *Aldosterone*, the hormone controlling the reabsorption of sodium in the kidney tubules is also concerned in sodium excretion by the sweat glands.

As mentioned earlier in the chapter, certain toxic elements like arsenic and the toxic but physiologically important copper are deposited in the hair. This is an excretory function of the hair follicles of the skin, since these elements are placed effectively outside of the body, and leave it when the hair is periodically shed, to be replaced by further new growth. We may note in passing that the body handles the dangerous heavy elements like barium, strontium, lead and radium in an analogous manner. These elements are deposited in an inert form in bone tissue.

The excretory functions of the alimentary canal

Small amounts of urea, amino acids, citric acid, calcium, chloride and phosphate ions, and certain drugs, are excreted in the *saliva*. Although most of these substances are reabsorbed, a small percentage leaves the body in the faeces.

Bile is a very important avenue for the excretion of a number of compounds, for instance excess cholesterol, the bile pigments, steroid hormones, iron, copper and a number of drugs.

The bile pigments, *bilirubin* and *biliverdin* are yellow and green pigments respectively formed during the catabolism of *haem*. Red blood cells live about 120 days and on dying are taken up by the cells of the *reticulo-endothelial system* (the R.E. cells), which are scattered throughout the tissues of the body. The haemoglobin released from the dead erythrocytes is split into haem and globin. The latter can be re-used for the synthesis of further haemoglobin. The haem is converted by the R.E. cells into bilirubin via verdohaemochromogen and biliverdin. The bilirubin is transported to the liver, bound to plasma albumin. In the parenchymal cells of the liver it is bound to two molecules of glucuronic acid and excreted in the bile as *bilirubin diglucuronide*. This compound gives bile its typical yellowish green appearance. Bilirubin diglucuronide is converted by the bacteria in the large intestine into urobilinogen, a colourless pigment, traces of which are reabsorbed and excreted in the urine. That which is unabsorbed is converted further by the gut flora into *urobilin*, also known as *stercobilin*, the brown colouring matter of the faeces. The small amounts of urobilinogen which are excreted in the urine do not normally contribute to the colour of freshly voided urine, since the compound is colourless. If a sample of urine is allowed to stand in contact with air, it slowly assumes a yellowish brown colour due to the conversion of urobilinogen to urobilin.

The sequence of events leading to the formulation of bilirubin can be readily observed when tissue is bruised. Initially the site of the bruise is reddish blue, due to the presence of damaged red cells and haemoglobin. As the latter is changed through verdohaemochromogen and biliverdin to bilirubin, so the bruise passes through various hues of bluish-green, greenish-yellow, to yellow, and grows fainter as the bilirubin is cleared by the blood circulation.

Blood plasma normally contains barely detectable amounts of bilirubin. When the blood plasma contains appreciable amounts of bilirubin the tissues of the body are stained distinctly yellow. The condition is known as *jaundice* or *icterus*, and occurs when:

(i) the breakdown of haemoglobin exceeds the capacity of the liver to excrete it as bilirubin diglucuronide. Since this is generally associated with an increased rate of red cell destruction, caused for instance by the malarial parasites, the condition is termed a *haemolytic icterus*.

(ii) the capacity of the parenchymal cells of the liver to form and excrete bilirubin is seriously impaired, e.g. in inflammatory conditions of the liver such as hepatitis. In this instance the jaundice is spoken of as a *hepato-cellular icterus*;

(iii) some mechanical obstruction to bile flow exists, for example a gallstone which occludes the bile duct. The bile which is being actively secreted all the time by the liver parenchymal cells commences to dam back into the liver and its components diffuse back into the liver cells and into the lymph spaces and blood circulation. In this instance, we term the condition an *obstructive icterus*. Large amounts of bilirubin glucuronide accumulating in the blood under these circumstances are cleared by the kidneys and appear in the urine, which assumes a deep yellowish-brown colour.

Various dyes which are specifically excreted in the bile are used to study liver function, for instance bromsulphalein. The rate at which an injected dose is cleared from the bloodstream by the liver is indicative of the integrity of the parenchymal cells of the liver. Various radio-opaque compounds, which are specifically excreted in the bile, are also used as contrast media in cholecystography, that is, the X-ray examination of the bile ducts and gall bladder.

The excretory functions of the *large intestine* were mentioned earlier in the chapter. Small amounts of urea and protein appear to be excreted through its walls into the faecal mass, whilst this is probably the main route by which calcium leaves the body.

CHAPTER 12

The Endocrine control of Physiological processes — The Vitamins

The regulating role of *hormones* has been mentioned several times in the earlier chapters. *Hormones* can be defined as *substances produced by certain tissues called endocrine glands and which are released into the blood and carried to other parts of the body where they exert a regulating effect on various physiological processes.* The study dealing with hormonal regulation is known as *Endocrinology.* In the present chapter only those aspects of endocrinology are discussed which have a direct bearing on biochemical processes in the body. It must be noted at this point that hormones perform their regulating functions in close association with the *autonomic nervous system.* A list of the most important endocrine glands and the hormones which they secrete is given in Table 12.1.

TABLE 12.1   The endocrine glands and their secretions

Gland	Hormones
Hypothalamus	releasing factors
	ADH, oxytoxin (both released in the neurohypophysis)
Adenohypophysis	STH, TSH, ACTH
	gonadotrophins
Pars intermedia	MSH
Thyroid	T_3, T_4, thyrocalcitonin
Parathyroid	parathormone
Islands of Langerhans	insulin, glucagon
Adrenal medulla	adrenalin, noradrenalin
Adrenal cortex	glucocorticoids, mineralocorticoids, androgens, oestrogens
Follicle of Graaf	oestrogens
Corpus luteum	progesterone
Testes	testosterone
Placenta	chorionic gonadotrophin
Digestive tract	gastrin, secretin, pancreozymin, enterocrinin, villikinin, enterogastrone
Kidneys	1,25-DHC
	erythropoietin
	renin
Tissues (general)	prostaglandins, histamine, bradykinin
Parasympathetic nerves	acetylcholine

The action of hormones — The negative feedback mechanism

The term hormone is derived from the Greek word *hormaein* meaning "to arouse or stimulate". When the term was coined all the hormones were known to stimulate, i.e., to increase the activity of the tissues or organs on which they acted. Presently some hormones are known which suppress (inhibit) the activity of their target organs or tissues. However, despite this objection, the term hormone is still in general use and is used in accordance with the definition given earlier.

The concept of negative feedback is a most important one in biological systems and is used with particular reference to the endocrine system. Generally speaking negative feedback control embraces the following considerations. We have a particular gland secreting a particular hormone. This controls a certain biochemical process, the reaction products of which must be maintained within a certain range of concentration in the blood and tissue fluids. As the concentration of these products reaches the upper value of this range, so they start to inhibit the production of the hormone concerned. As the concentration of the products falls to the lower value in the range so the inhibiting (or negative feedback) influence is abolished; the hormone is secreted once more and the reaction products commence to accumulate again. The control of the blood sugar level is a striking example of this phenomenon. As the blood sugar level falls, so the adrenal medulla responds by secreting adrenalin, which stimulates the conversion of liver glycogen to glucose. As the blood sugar level rises towards the upper limit of its normal concentration so the secretion of adrenalin is abolished.

There are three ways by which hormones can exercise their action on their target organs or tissues.

1. By the repression or derepression of genes (chapter 8). For example, the growth hormone acts in this way.

2. Through the action of cyclic AMP or other cyclic nucleotides (chapter 7). This is the way in which adrenalin and glucagon act.

3. By influencing the transport of substances (e.g. electrolytes, glucose and amino acids) across cell membranes. The precise mechanism of this kind of hormone action is still unknown. One example of this is the action of insulin, which stimulates the transport of glucose from the blood into the cells of various tissues.

The action of some hormones is confined to a single target organ or tissue, for example thyrotrophic hormone (also called thyroid stimulating hormone or TSH) acts only upon the thyroid. Other hormones act upon discrete areas of certain structures within certain organs, for instance antidiuretic hormone (ADH) acts upon the cells of the distal convoluted tubules of the nephrons in the kidney. A further group of hormones, for instance the thyroid hormones and the growth hormone (also known as somatotrophic hormone or STH) act upon a very wide range of body tissues.

The chemical nature of hormones

The various hormones produced in the endocrine glands can be grouped under a few headings depending on their chemical structure:

1. *Polypeptide hormones:* the hormones produced by the hypothalamus, adenohypophysis, islands of Langerhans, parathyroid glands and the gastro-intestinal tract.

2. *Amino acid derivatives:* hormones of the adrenal medulla and the thyroid.

3. *Steroids:* the hormones of the adrenal cortex, ovaries and testes.

4. *Cyclic fatty acids:* the prostaglandins, produced by a variety of tissues.

The organization of the endocrine system and the hypothalamus

The endocrine glands fall into two groups according to how their functions are controlled and organized:

(a) Those that are influenced to a large degree by the hypothalamus and the autonomic system.

(b) Those that function independently of such control.

The hypothalamus, which is often referred to in lighter vein as "the conductor of the endocrine orchestra" occupies a central role in the regulation of the endocrine system. In it are centres controlling some of the basic functions necessary for the survival of the individual, for instance the centres controlling the thirst mechanism, sweating and the regulation of the water balance. With regard to the latter certain cells in the hypothalamus secrete the hormone, antidiuretic hormone. In it are the centres regulating appetite, the control of body heat and some of the sexual functions. With regard to the latter, certain cells in the hypothalamus secrete the hormone, oxytocin.

It receives nerve connections from various levels of the brain, and from receptors scattered throughout the body, monitoring the functions mentioned as well as others. It is connected by neuro-secretory tracts to the neurohypophysis and since it houses the sympathetic centre fibres proceed from it to many tissues receiving sympathetic innervation, prominent amongst which is the adrenal medulla.

It regulates the secretions of the adenohypophysis in response to a wide variety of stimuli arising both within and without the body. It performs this function by secreting releasing factors, which stimulate the formation and release of the hormones secreted by the adenohypophysis. These hormones stimulate the activity of a number of endocrine glands and one of them, somatotrophin (or growth hormone) stimulates anabolic processes throughout the body, particularly protein synthesis.

A particularly close association thus exists between the nervous system and the endocrine system and this association is particularly seen in one structure that serves both systems, the hypothalamus. It is scarcely surprising that the emotions can have a profound effect on certain endocrine phenomena, for instance the menstrual cycle in the female. By the same token certain hormones can exert a profound effect on behaviour of persons and animals.

The classification of the hormones according to their functions

The list of hormones presented in Table 12.1 is a lengthy one. A detailed discussion of the functions of each hormone and the interrelationship of these functions, with the functions of the other hormones is largely beyond the scope of this work. In order to understand how the hormones regulate metabolic processes, they have been grouped according to the functions which they perform as follows:

A. Hormones that regulate the calcium and phosphate content of the body.

B. Hormones that regulate the water, sodium and potassium content of the body.

C. Hormones that regulate metabolic processes involving carbohydrates, fats and proteins.

D. Hormones that regulate reproductive functions.

E. Hormones of the digestive tract.

F. Hormones that regulate the functions of endocrine glands — the trophic hormones and releasing factors.

G. Miscellaneous hormones.

Hormones that regulate the calcium and phosphate content of the body

(The student is referred to chapter 3 for further details of this group of hormones.)

1. *Thyrocalcitonin*

Functions: (a) It stimulates the deposition of calcium in bone tissue, and (b) decreases the blood calcium concentration.

Endocrine gland concerned: the thyroid (a large gland in the neck situated in front and on both sides of the trachea).

Stimulus for secretion: High blood calcium concentration, which is registered by the cells secreting the hormone.

2. *Parathormone*

Functions: (*a*) The release of calcium from bone tissue; (*b*) the inhibition of phosphate reabsorption in the kidney tubules; (*c*) by these means blood calcium concentration is increased; and (*d*) the blood phosphate concentration is decreased.

Endocrine gland: parathyroid (four small glands located on the surface of the thyroid).

Stimulus for secretion: A low blood calcium concentration, registered by the secreting cells themselves.

3. 1,25-*dihydroxycholecalciferol* (1,25-DHC).

Functions: (*a*) It stimulates calcium absorption in the small intestine, and (*b*) increases the blood calcium concentration.

Endocrine gland: the kidneys (see chapter 3).

Stimulus for secretion: A low blood calcium concentration which is monitored by (*a*) the kidney cells concerned, and (*b*) the parathyroid, by the release of parathormone.

Note: A deficiency of 1,25 DHC, due to an inadequate intake of vitamin D or to insufficient exposure of the body to ultra-violet rays or sunlight leads to serious disturbances in calcium metabolism. A deficiency of parathormone has the same effect.

4. *Oestrogens*

These control the deposition of Ca^{++} in the bones during puberty.

5. *Testosterone*

This increases the deposition of calcium ions in the bones by stimulating the production of the bone matrix on which calcium is deposited.

Hormones that regulate the water, sodium and potassium content of the body

(The attention of the student is drawn to chapters 3 and 5 where these hormones are discussed.)

1. *Antidiuretic hormone* (ADH)

Functions: (*a*) To increase water reabsorption in the kidneys. This increases the water content of the body and has the effect of lowering the concentrations of electrolytes like sodium and potassium ions, in the blood.

Endocrine gland: The hypothalamus. The hormone is transported to the neurohypothesis by the axons of the cells producing it and is stored there until its release is initiated by nerve impulses travelling along the same axons.

Stimuli for secretion: A high electrolyte concentration of the blood, which can mean either a diminution of plasma and total body water or an increase of the electrolyte content of the body.

Other effects: In high concentration it causes vasoconstriction hence the synonyms which are sometimes used are *vasopressin* and *pitressin*.

2. *Aldosterone*

Functions: (*a*) By increasing sodium reabsorption in the kidney tubules it raises the concentration of sodium in the blood; and as a result of this (*b*) it stimulates the simultaneous reabsorption of some water due to osmotic effects; (*c*) simultaneously with these effects potassium secretion in the kidney tubules is promoted, which has the effect of lowering the plasma potassium levels.

Endocrine gland: Adrenal cortex.

Stimuli for secretion: (*a*) A low sodium concentration in the blood, or (*b*) a high potassium concentration in the blood, or (*c*) a reduced plasma water level.

3. *Testosterone and Progesterone*

Testosterone and other androgens and progesterone have the effect of stimulating some degree of sodium and water reabsorption in the kidney tubules. The reabsorption of water is also stimulated to some degree by the oestrogens.

Hormones that regulate metabolic processes involving carbohydrates, fats and proteins (see chapter 10)

1. *Growth hormone (somatotrophin,* STH)

Functions: (*a*) It promotes the growth of cells and tissues, by stimulating protein synthesis. The overall effect is due to (i) increased amino acid transport into the cells, and (ii) stimulation of RNA synthesis. (*b*) It tends to inhibit the utilization of glucose by certain tissues, e.g. the muscles by (i) inhibiting the transport of glucose into the cells of this tissue, and by (ii) inhibiting glycolysis, and by (iii) stimulating gluconeogenesis. These phenomena have the effect of (iv) increasing the blood sugar concentration, and (v) stimulating the secretion of insulin by the islands of Langerhans. (*c*) It stimulates the mobilisation of fat for the production of energy. The overall effect is due to (i) stimulation of lipolysis, (ii) inhibition of lipogenesis. These effects lead to an increased fatty acid level in the blood.

Endocrine gland: The acidophilic cells of the adenohypophysis.

Stimuli for secretion: Somatotrophin is secreted throughout the life of an individual but is particularly active during growth. The regulation of its secretion and the response of tissues to it is a complex phenomenon and is largely beyond the scope of this discussion. Insufficient production of the hormone before puberty leads to *dwarfism*, i.e. retarded, but normally proportioned growth. Oversecretion of the hormone before puberty leads to *gigantism*, the individual once more having normal proportions. Oversecretion after puberty leads to *acromegaly*, a form of gigantism in which the extremeties of the body are enlarged.

2. Insulin

Functions: (a) It stimulates the transport of glucose into the cells of certain tissues as explained in chapter 10. This tends to lower the concentration of glucose in the blood and favours the synthesis of glycogen in muscle and adipose tissue; (b) it stimulates the uptake of amino acids by cells; (c) it stimulates protein synthesis and inhibits the use of amino acids for energy production; and (d) it stimulates lipogenesis.

Endocrine organ: The β-cells of the Islands of Langerhans.

Stimuli for secretion: (a) A high glucose concentration in blood, or (b) a high concentration of long chain fatty acids in blood, or (c) a high concentration of certain amino acids in blood notably arginine and lysine.

Note: The disease condition, *diabetes mellitus* has been mentioned a number of times in the foregoing chapters We have taken note of the fact that it is due to an inadequate production of insulin; and this leads to an inability on the part of many tissues to utilize glucose. The result is a high level of glucose in the blood (*hyperglycaemia*), so high in fact that the transport maximum for glucose in the kidney tubules is exceeded and glucose appears in the urine (*glucosuria*). We have noted that the failure to utilize glucose leads to increased lipolysis and ultimately to an accumulation of aceto-acetic acid and related compounds in the blood (*ketosis*). These compounds bring about a state of metabolic *acidosis* and also appear in the urine in appreciable amounts (*ketonuria*).

One useful test used in the diagnosis of diabetes mellitus is the *glucose tolerance test*. The patient is given a standard dose of glucose. In the normal individual there is a rapid rise in the blood glucose levels to about 150mg/100ml blood. The blood glucose concentration then returns to normal within the course of the next two hours. In the diabetic, the rise in blood sugar is greater and is sustained, slowly returning to the pre-dosing value over a number of hours.

Patients with a tumour of the Islands of Langerhans produce excessive amounts of insulin. This lowers the blood sugar markedly (*hypoglycaemia*). The same is seen following over-dosage with insulin. Many individuals often produce excessive amounts of insulin in the absence of any tumours, but in response to a high carbohydrate intake. The ensuing hypoglycaemia is characterised by weakness, dizziness, sweating, some confusion and in severe cases, coma.

3. *Glucagon*

Functions: (*a*) It stimulates glycogenolysis, mainly in the liver but also to a lesser extent in the muscle tissue. It thus tends to raise the blood glucose concentration; (*b*) it stimulates lipolysis.

Endocrine organs: (*a*) The α-cells of the Islands of Langerhans; (*b*) the mucous membrane of the small intestine (enteroglucagon).

Stimulus for secretion: A decrease in the glucose concentration of the blood.

4. *Cortisol*

Cortisol and the other *glucocorticoids*, e.g. cortisone have been mentioned frequently in the discussions on metabolism in the previous chapters. The hormone is released, amongst other things, in response to stress.

Functions: (*a*) It stimulates gluconeogenesis thus raising the blood glucose concentration and stimulating the formation of liver glycogen; (*b*) it stimulates RNA synthesis in the liver, this leading in turn to increased protein synthesis; (*c*) it stimulates the secretion of hydrochloric acid, pepsinogen and trypsinogen in the alimentary canal, thus promoting the digestion of proteins.

Endocrine organ: Adrenal cortex.

Stimulus for secretion: The response of the body to stress is a complex one, involving a number of neurohormonal mechanisms. Depletion of liver glycogen and a falling blood sugar level result amongst other things in the liberation of the adreno-corticotrophic hormone (ACTH, see later), which stimulates cortisol production.

Note: (i) Ascorbic acid (vitamin C) is necessary for the synthesis of the steroid hormones of the adrenal cortex. Hormones of this type, being steroids are insoluble in water. They are transported in the blood-stream from the cells producing them, to their target tissues by specific plasma protein carriers. (ii) Cortisol is transported in the blood by the protein *transcortin*. (iii) In doses considerably higher than the normal blood levels of these compounds, they have an anti-inflammatory action and are much used in medicine and surgery for this effect.

5. *Adrenalin* (also known as *epinephrine*)

This hormone is produced by the adrenal medulla together with the closely related *noradrenalin* (norepinephrine) and *dopamine*. Since these compounds are related to the phenolic compound catechol, they are often referred to as the *catecholamines*.

Functions: Adrenalin places the body in a favourable position to react to adverse circumstances by (a) Stimulating glycogenolysis in muscle and liver, and thus increasing the blood sugar and the rate of glycolysis in muscle tissue; (b) stimulating lipolysis in adipose tissue and thus increasing the concentration of fatty acids in the blood. This effect is shared by noradrenalin; (c) it increases the heart rate, blood pressure and cardiac output; (d) it causes vaso-constriction of the blood vessels of the skin, kidneys and visceral organs and causes vaso-dilation in muscle tissue, liver and heart muscle. Noradrenalin is a general vasoconstrictor; (e) it increases the depth and frequency of respiration; (f) it inhibits the movements of the alimentary canal, bladder and stimulates the closure of the sphinctres of these organs.

Endocrine organ: Adrenal medulla.

Stimuli for secretion: Stimulation of the autonomous nervous system before and during activity and in emotional states such as anger, anxiety and so on.

Note: Large amounts of noradrenalin are produced at the sympathetic nerve endings. Noradrenalin is also a transmitter substance in brain tissue.

6. *The Thyroid Hormones* (thyroxin, also known as tetra-iodothyronine or T_4 and tri-iodothyronine, T_3).

Functions: (i) These hormones increase the amount of free heat available in cells as explained in chapter 10. By doing so they stimulate metabolic processes in general; (ii) during the years of growth, this action is particularly important and promotes growth of the individual. In this respect, the thyroid hormones act in unison with somatotrophin. The growth of certain tissues, particularly the brain, is markedly promoted by the thyroid hormones; (iii) growth and development of connective tissues is further promoted by virtue of the fact that these hormones stimulate the conversion of the precursors of vitamin A (the carotenes) to vitamin A in the mucosa of the small intestine. Vitamin A is required for the synthesis of certain connective tissue components and for the maintenance of the integrity of mucous membranes.

Endocrine organ: the thyroid gland.

Stimulus for secretion: Any circumstances which require increased heat production. The secretion of these hormones is the result of the action on the thyroid of thyrotrophic hormone. This hormone is secreted by the adenohypophysis in response to a specific releasing factor put out by the hypothalamus. As noted earlier the hypothalamus receives information from all over the body and reacts accordingly.

Note: As the names of these hormones suggest, iodine is present in their molecules. This is the only known biological function of iodine but it is none the less a vital one (chapter 3). There are many regions in the world where iodine is deficient in the soil and drinking water. The population of these areas are thus exposed to an iodine deficiency and show signs of an iodine deficiency. The most prominent of these signs is the development of a goitre, the name given to a markedly enlarged thyroid gland. Affected individuals do not have sufficient iodine present in their bodies for adequate synthesis of the thyroid hormones. Since these compounds are not present in amounts sufficient to suppress the secretion of thyrotrophic hormone (TTH) by negative feedback, this hormone continues to act upon the thyroid gland, stimulating its continued growth, hence the development of the goitre.

A simple remedial measure which can be used on a wide scale in the areas where goitre is endemic (the name is from the Greek *en demos*, literally "prevalent amongst men") is the use of iodized salt in the preparation and consumption of foods.

Children born of mothers suffering from goitre are born with an iodine deficiency. Such children show retarded growth and since the thyroid hormones are necessary for brain development, show also considerable mental deficiency. These unfortunates are often referred to as *cretins* and the condition as *cretinism.* (The name is a particularly unkind one. Although often taken to refer to the inhabitants of Crete where cases of the disease occur, it is in fact a French corruption, *Crétin* of the Latin *Christianus*, which was used in a derogatory sense by the Roman authorities to mean "a barely human creature". The word cretin is still used today in a derogatory sense.)

7. *The Sex Hormones*

Although the action of these hormones is primarily on the organs of reproduction, and on the regulation of the female sexual cycle, the androgens, oestrogens and progesterone have a significant action on various aspects of protein, fat and carbohydrate metabolism.

The oestrogens and the androgens (e.g. testosterone) stimulate the development of the secondary sex characteristics. This action includes the development of the typical male or female skeleton, the development of the typical texture of the hair and skin of males and females, the distribution of hair in males and females, the deposition of fat in the female body and the development of the organs of reproduction and the mammae. All this implies a subtle action on protein synthesis, probably at the level of RNA and DNA, and on the synthesis of complex lipid and carbohydrate components of tissues.

The trophic hormones and releasing factors

The adjective trophic denotes that which has a nurturing, nutrient or growth promoting function. It is derived from the Greek *trephō*, to nourish or from *trophos*, one who cultivates, cares for or nurtures. The trophic hormones are therefore concerned with the growth, development and secretion of tissues, specifically those of the endocrine glands. The group includes *somatotrophic hormone* (growth hormone or STH), having a general trophic effect on the body; *thyrotrophic hormone* (TTH, or thyroid stimulating hormone TSH), acting upon the thyroid gland; *adrenocorticotrophic hormone* (ACTH), acting upon the adrenal cortex; and the *gonadotrophic hormones* (follicle stimulating hormone, FSH; luteinising hormone, LH, luteotrophic hormone, LTH; and the male equivalents of these), which act upon the organs of reproduction (the gonads). One encounters these names frequently spelt with the suffix *-tropic* or *-tropin*. This is an unfortunate Americanism, which has crept into fairly general usage. This suffix is derived from the Greek, *tropos*, a turning or way and does not reflect accurately the intended meaning of *-trophic*. Not only do the trophic hormones stimulate the growth and development of the glands mentioned but they stimulate the release of the hormones produced by these glands.

The trophic hormones are produced and secreted by the adenohyphophysis in response to the stimulus presented by *releasing factors* (*librins*) secreted by the hypothalamus. There is for each trophic hormone a specific releasing factor, and in a few instances the hypothalamus is known to produce *inhibiting factors* (*statins*) which inhibit further secretion of the trophic hormone concerned, e.g., luteotrophic hormone inhibiting factor and somatostatin.

Thyrotrophic hormone stimulates the uptake of iodine by the thyroid gland, in addition to stimulating the secretion of the thyroid hormones and stimulation of development of the thyroid.

Melanocyte Stimulating Hormone (MSH) is a trophic hormone produced by the cells of the *pars intermedia* of the hypophysis. This hormone stimulates the growth and development of the melanocytes (the pigment producing cells of the skin) and the production of the pigment, melanin by these cells.

The hormones that regulate reproductive functions

The organs of reproduction are the gonads; the testes in the male and the ovaries in the female. Certain cells in the testes produce the androgens (or male hormones) like testosterone, but the ovary is a more complex structure in that the oestrogens (female hormones) are largely produced by the follicles of Graaf and progesterone by the corpus luteum. The follicles and the corpus luteum develop in the functioning ovary and also secrete their hormones at different times during the female sexual (or menstrual) cycle.

1. *Testosterone*

This is the most important androgen. As already noted it stimulates the development of the male secondary sex characteristics probably by stimulating the synthesis of specific proteins.

Secretion: It is secreted by the interstitial (or Leydig) cells of the testes in response to *interstitial cell stimulating hormone* (ISSH), the male counterpart of follicle stimulating hormone (FSH). It is produced from a very early moment in life, stimulating the development of the gonads in the foetus and the descent of the testes at birth. Larger amounts are secreted from puberty onwards.

Functions: Besides those already mentioned it stimulates the final maturation of the spermatozoa. The production of spermatozoa is stimulated by *spermatogenesis stimulating hormone* (SSH) the male counterpart of luteinising hormone (LH) secreted by the adenohypophysis.

2. *The Oestrogens*

As noted earlier these are produced by the follicles of Graaf. They are produced during the first part of each menstrual cycle in response to the stimulus presented by FSH.

Functions: (a) They stimulate the development of the secondary sex characteristics in the female; (b) they stimulate the growth and development of the uterus and fallopian tubes, the ovaries and the external genitalia; (c) they bring about cyclic alterations in the nature of the vaginal mucosa and its secretions; (d) they stimulate the proliferation of the duct system in the mammary glands.

Note: In this list of functions the oestrogens are indicated by the plural "they". The group includes *oestrone, oestradiol* and *oestriol*, the three main oestrogens.

3. *Progesterone*

This hormone is produced by the *corpus luteum* which develops in the cavity left when the ripe follicle of Graaf ruptures under the influence of luteinising hormone (LH) and liberates the ovum into the fallopian tubes. This process (ovulation) occurs at the middle of the menstrual cycle. The corpus luteum grows and secretes progesterone in the latter half of the cycle.

Functions: (a) It prepares the endometrium of the uterus to receive a fertilized ovum (whether fertilization takes place or not). It does this by stimulating the growth and secretions of the endometrial cells and by increasing the vascularity of the endometrium; (b) it stimulates the growth of the glandular part of the mammary glands.

Note: Progesterone has a marked stimulatory effect on the reabsorption of water, sodium and chloride ions in the distal portions of the kidney tubules. This is seen as some degree of water retention and contributes to the increase in body mass experienced by many women in the latter part of the menstrual cycle. Since one of the major functions of progesterone is the maintenance of pregnancy, this water retaining effect contributes to the general increase in body mass experienced during pregnancy.

4. *Hormones produced by the Placenta*

The placenta produces at different times during pregnancy variable amounts of oestrogens, progesterone and *chorionic gonadotrophin*. The latter has largely the effect of stimulating the production of further progesterone by the corpus luteum.

The hormones of the digestive tract

These hormones, which include *gastrin, secretin, pancreozymin-cholecystokinin, enterogastrone, enterocrinin* and *villikinin* have been dealt with in chapter 9. The attention of the student is drawn to the relevant discussion.

Miscellaneous hormones

The *prostaglandins* are a group of related cyclic fatty acids produced by many tissues in the body, e.g. the lungs, liver, uterus and gastrointestinal tract. The functions of most of them are still ill-understood at this stage. Some act by stimulating the formation of the general metabolic activator, cyclic AMP. Others act by promoting the degradation of this compound. In general they promote blood circulation by bringing about vasodilatation. They appear to increase the permeability of capillaries and thus promote the exchange of nutrients for waste products at this level. Some of them appear to stimulate the movement of sodium, potassium and chloride ions across cell membranes. Some stimulate the movements of the digestive tract and at least one is concerned with the contraction of the musculature of the pregnant uterus at parturition.

Erythropoietin is produced by certain cells in the liver and kidneys in response to hypoxia. It stimulates the production of erythrocytes by the red bone-marrow.

Angiotensin is a substance which produces vasoconstriction and which stimulates the release of aldosterone by the adrenal cortex. Since aldosterone stimulates the reabsorption of sodium ions and water in the kidney tubules it has the effect of increasing the blood volume. The sum of these effects is an increase in the systemic blood pressure and in the rate of blood circulation. When the blood pressure falls or when the rate of perfusion through the kidneys is slow a mild hypoxia develops in these organs. In close association with the glomeruli of each nephron is a group of cells known as the *juxtaglomerular apparatus*. These cells liberate the enzyme *renin* in response to the hypoxic conditions. Renin acts upon one of the blood plasma globulins known as *angiotensinogen*, bringing about the liberation of angiotensin in the circulating blood. It then brings about the rise in blood pressure and the increase in the circulatory rate, by the effects mentioned, thus alleviating the hypoxic conditions pertaining in the kidneys.

THE VITAMINS

The vitamins are a group of compounds which are generally regarded as being essential for life and which must be present in sufficient amounts in the diet. In the event of a deficiency of one or more of these vitamins, well-defined symptoms, characteristic of the particular deficiency, will make their appearance. The name vitamin is an old one, dating back to the earlier part of this century. One of the first deficiency states to be studied was the disease known as *beri-beri*, a condition very prevalent in the Far East (hence the Javanese name) and elsewhere in the world. It was found at that time, that the symptoms of the disease were due to a deficiency of thiamine (vitamin B_1), and that the symptoms could be alleviated by foodstuffs rich in this compound. Since thiamine is an amine and was necessary for life the term "vitamine" was introduced. The term has been retained as a name for accessory food factors, which are neither amino acids nor trace elements.

It was generally held that these substances were not formed in the bodies of the animal species requiring them, and that they must be provided in the diet. With the state of our present knowledge on this topic it is necessary to modify this concept somewhat. A number of these compounds do in fact happen to be formed in the animal body, but in amounts which are inadequate to meet the body's needs. The vitamins play a vital role in metabolism. As far as we know all of them are either *co-enzymes* or part of the molecules of various co-enzymes. In the latter event, they are generally the functional part of the co-enzyme molecule.

Since vitamins are so intimately concerned with metabolism, we would expect to find the highest concentrations of these substances in the organs of plants and animals that possess the highest metabolic activity. This is indeed so, the richest sources of vitamins being liver, heart, kidneys, the seeds of plants (which we utilize as cereals of different sorts), green leaves (of the leaf-vegetables for instance) and roots (for instance, the root-crops such as carrots, beets and potatoes). Two other very important sources of vitamins are milk and eggs, and the various food products derived from these. Milk is, for the initial period of a mammal's life, the only food which the suckling ingests. The contents of an egg constitute the only nourishment available to a developing chick embryo. Both milk and eggs contain therefore all the nutrients necessary for growth and development. (It should be noted, however, that some of these nutrients, such as iron in milk are not present in amounts sufficient to meet the needs of the suckling, once it commences to grow rapidly.) It should be noted in passing that many cf the best sources of vitamins are also the best sources of proteins and minerals. For this reason, the nutritional deficiency diseases, which are so prevalent amongst the undernourished population groups in the world, are generally compound deficiencies.

The large intestine of mammals and man supports a very large population of micro-organisms which live in symbiosis with the individual. This population, which consists of a wide variety of bacteria, yeasts and protozoa, lives upon undigested food residues, from which they derive energy. In return for this they provide much in the way of fatty acids, essential amino acids and a number of vitamins. Notable amongst the latter are the vitamins K (see below).

The vitamins were originally named by according to them letters of the alphabet, e.g. vitamins A, C, D and so on. This became most confusing when a number of compounds were grouped together as the vitamin B complex and named vitamins B_1, B_2, B_3, B_6, B_{12}, etc. As the list grew and as compounds were removed from the list, so the system of nomenclature became unwieldy. Today the general tendency is to keep the names Vitamins A, C, D and E and to call all the other vitamins (the so-called vitamin B complex) by more meaningful trivial or systematic names, e.g. thiamine, nicotinic acid, pyridoxine and so on.

In order to make our study of the vitamins easier it is convenient to place them into two groups according to some common physical properties or physiological functions:

(a) *The Fat-soluble Vitamins:* The group includes vitamins A, D, E and K. They share in common the fact that they are associated with the lipid components of cells and are extractable with the usual fat solvents. In each instance the name of the vitamin covers a number of related compounds, and we speak of the vitamins A or the vitamins E, and so on. The vitamins A and D are present in plants in the form of precursor substances which are converted in the body to the active vitamins.

There are two *vitamins A*, namely A_1 and A_2 (also called the *retinols*). The precursors, which occur widely in nature in the green parts of plants, in cereals such as maize, and in many root vegetables and fruits, are known as *carotenes*. They are converted to the vitamins A in the mucosa of the small intestine and in the liver, and are then stored in the liver. The richest sources of the vitamins A are the oils obtained from the livers of various fish species, e.g. cod liver oil, and the oils obtained from hake and shark liver. The carotenes are also present in animal products such as eggs, milk and cheese. Although present in these animal products, they are still of plant origin and are secreted by the maternal animal in the egg-yolk or milk, to be available to the developing chick embryo or suckling, as the case may be.

The vitamins A are mainly concerned in the synthesis of various tissue polysaccharides and in the conversion of light energy into nerve impulses as part of the phenomenon of vision.

There are two vitamins D, notably *calciferol* (D_2) and *cholecalciferol* (D_3). The main precursors of these vitamins are *7-dehydrocholesterol* and *ergosterol*. These compounds, like the carotenes and the vitamins E and K are absorbed from the digestive tract in the form of water-soluble associations with the bile acids. They are stored in the body fats. The richest sources of these precursors and of the vitamins D are the fish liver oils mentioned above, the precursors being present in appreciable amounts in fresh vegetables, fruit, cereals, milk and eggs. The precursors are converted into calciferol and cholecalciferol in the skin, by the action of ultra-violet rays present in sunlight. These products are converted in the kidneys to the active form of vitamin D, the hormone *1,25-dihydroxycholecalciferol* (1,25-DHC) which is intimately concerned with the absorption of calcium from the digestive tract. This function is vital for the adequate calcification of bones and teeth.

There are at least eight vitamins E. They are a group of closely related compounds collectively called the *tocopherols*. They are of plant origin and are absorbed from the digestive tract and used as such. They occur mainly in cell membranes, where they function as anti-oxidants, i.e. they protect unsaturated fatty acids and other lipids against oxidation.

A number of vitamins K are known. Like the vitamins E, they are of plant origin and are used as such by man and animals. The bacterial flora in the large intestine represent one of the major sources of these vitamins for us. The vitamins K are concerned with the synthesis of prothrombin in the liver. This compound is one of the substances involved in the clotting of blood.

(*b*) *The Water-soluble Vitamins:* This group includes those compounds generally classed as the vitamins B, as well as vitamin C. The vitamins B are all part of various co-enzymes concerned with phenomena such as oxidation and reduction reactions, the transfer of various radicals from one compound to another, and with the synthesis of various substances. These vitamins are present in the largest amounts in those organs of plants or animals which have the greatest metabolic activity, as mentioned earlier. The best sources of these vitamins are thus vegetables and fruits, cereals, liver, heart, kidneys, milk and eggs. Significant amounts of these vitamins are formed for us by the bacterial flora in the large intestine.

The various vitamins B, the co-enzymes of which they are part and the functions of these co-enzymes are listed in Table 12.2.

TABLE 12.2   The Vitamins B

Vitamin	Co-enzyme	Function
Thiamine (B_1)	Thiamine pyrophosphate	decarboxylation reactions
Riboflavin (B_2)	FAD	hydrogen carrier
Nicotinic Acid (B_3)	NAD, NADP	hydrogen carriers
Pyridoxine (B_6)	Pyridoxal phosphate	amino group carrier
Pantothenic Acid	Co-enzyme A	metabolic activator
Biotin	Biotin-containing proteins	CO_2 carrier
Folic Acid	Tetrahydrofolic acid	"one-carbon" metabolism
Cyanocobalamine (B_{12})	Cobamide co-enzymes	intra-molecular re-arrangements

Ascorbic acid (vitamin C) is widely distributed in the body. It is a powerful reducing agent and takes part in various intracellular reactions as a hydrogen carrier. It is also concerned with the absorption of iron in the small intestine.

Appendix A

actinium (Ac)
alabamine (astatine, helvetium) (At)
alumin(i)um (Al)
americium (Am)
antimony (stibium) (Sb)
argon (Ar)
arsenic (As)
astatine (alabamine, helvetium) (At)

barium (Ba)
berkelium (Bk)
beryllium (glucinum) (Be)
bismuth (Bi)
boron (B)
bromin(e) (Br)

cadmium (Cd)
c(a)esium (Cs)
calcium (Ca)
californium (Cf)
carbon (C)
cerium (Ce)
cesium (Cs)
chlorin(e) (Cl)
chromium (Cr)
cobalt (Co)
columbium (niobium) (Cb)
copper (Cu)
curium (Cm)

dysprosium (Dy)

einsteinium (Es)
erbium (Er)
europium (Eu)

fermium (Fm)
florentium (illinium, promethium) (Pm)
fluorin(e) (F)
francium (virginium) (Fr)

gadolinium (Gd)
gallium (Ga)
geranium (Ge)
glucinum (beryllium) (Be)

gold (Au)

hafnium (Hf)
helium (He)
helvetium (alabamine, astatine) (At)
holmium (Ho)
hydrogen (H)

ilinium (florentium, promethium) (Pm)
indium (In)
iodin(e) (I)
iridium (Ir)
iron (Fe)

krypton (Kr)

lanthanum (La)
lawrencium (Lw)
lead (Pb)
lithium (Li)
lutetium (Lu)

magnesium (Mg)
manganese (Mn)
masurium (technetium) (Tc)
mendelevium (Md)
mercury (quicksilver) (Hg)
molybdenum (Mo)

neodymium (Nd)
neon (Ne)
neptunium (Np)
nickel (Ni)
niobium (columbium) (Nb)
niton (radium emanation, radon) (Rn)
nitrogen (N)
nobelium (No)

osmium (Os)
oxygen (O)

palladium (Pd)
phosphorus (P)
platinum (Pt)
plutonium (Pu)
polonium (Po)
potassium (K)

praseodymium (Pr)
promethium (florentium, illinium) (Pm)
prot(o)actinium (Pa)

quicksilver (mercury) (Hg)

radium (Ra)
radium emanation (niton, radon) (Rn)
rhenium (Re)
rhodium (Rh)
rubidium (Rb)
ruthenium (Ru)

samarium (Sm)
scandium (Sc)
selenium (Se)
silicium (silicon) (Si)
silver (Ag)
sodium (Na)
stibium (antimony) (Sb)
strontium (Sr)
sulfur (sulphur) (S)

tantalum (Ta)
technetium (masurium) (Tc)
tellurium (Te)
terbium (Tb)
thallium (Tl)
thorium (Th)
thulium (Tm)
tin (Sn)
titanium (Ti)
tungsten (wolfram) (W)

uranium (U)

vanadium (V)
virginium (francium) (Fr)

wolfram (tungsten) (W)

xenon (Xe)

ytterbium (Yb)
yttrium (Y)

zinc (Zn)
zirconium (Zr)

Appendix B

1. Give the definition and an example of (a) a material, (b) a substance, (c) an element, and (d) a compound.
2. Describe the structure of (a) an atom, (b) an ion, and (c) a molecule.
3. Explain the terms *atomic number* and *atomic mass*.
4. For what purpose is energy necessary in the body and in what forms does it occur.
5. Discuss the *states of matter* in terms of temperature and molecular movement.
6. Discuss the mechanisms and importance of *oxidative processes* in the body.
7. Discuss briefly the handling of oxygen by the body.
8. Write notes about the various types of *anoxias*.
9. Describe some medical uses of oxygen.
10. What is the physiological importance of *hydrogen, carbon* and *nitrogen*?
11. Describe *active transport* in connection with sodium in the body.
12. What is the role of *calcium* in the body and in which foods is it found?
13. Discuss the role of *Vitamin D* in connection with the calcium content of the body.
14. Discuss the role of calcium in connection with *blood clotting*.
15. What is the importance of *iron* in the body and what happens when there is a deficiency of this element?
16. Name five *trace elements* and indicate their functions.
17. Explain, with examples, the way *ions* and *molecules* are formed.
18. Discuss the formation of single and double *covalent* bonds.
19. Give examples of six *ions* and six *radicals*.
20. Discuss the factors that influence the rate of chemical reactions.
21. You have to prepare 80mg *sodium hydroxide*. Calculate the required amount of sodium and water to be used for this purpose.
22. Discuss the way in which *water* is distributed throughout the body and name the hormones that play a role in this connection.
23. Describe the process of *dissociation* and define the *dissociation constant*.
24. Define *pH* and discuss the terms *acid, base* and *neutral*.
25. Discuss, with example the formation of *salts*.
26. Define the terms *suspension, solution* and *emulsion*.
27. Discuss the ways by which *water* can be *lost* from the body.
28. Describe the formation of urine.
29. Write notes about *fluid exchange* in the capillaries.
30. Discuss *buffers*.
31. What is a *hydrocarbon*? Which hydrocarbons are found in nature?

32. What are cyclic hydrocarbons?
33. Write a paragraph about *ethanol* indicating how it is formed in the nature, its properties and uses.
34. What is an *amino acid*? How are proteins formed from them?
35. Which class of *monosaccharides* is of physiological importance? Name three examples and write a few sentences about each of them (where they are found in nature, properties of importance, etc.).
36. How do *starches, dextrins, cellulose* and *glycogen* differ from each other?
37. How are *triglycerides* made up and what is their physiological importance?
38. Name the *bile pigments*. How are they formed in the body and how are they eliminated from it?
39. Define: *nucleosides, nucleotides* and *nucleic acids.*
40. Describe briefly the way *DNA* and *RNA* molecules differ from each other.
41. Explain briefly the terms *primary, secondary* and *tertiary* structure of proteins.
42. Explain *oxidative phosphorylation* and *the electron transport system.*
43. Give a short *classification* of the different types of enzymes that are found in the body.
44. Give a short description of the way *enzymes* act on their substrates.
45. Explain the terms *trace elements, proenzymes, reversible reactions.*
46. Name and discuss briefly the functions of *water soluble vitamins.*
47. Discuss the physiological functions of *fat soluble vitamins.*
48. Explain the way in which *calcium* and *phosphate* metabolism is regulated by vitamin D and by the hormones of the parathyroid and thyroid.
49. What is *cyclic AMP*? How is it formed and what is its importance?
50. Name and discuss briefly the hormones that stimulate the secretion of the different *digestive juices.*
51. Discuss the factors that are important in the *absorbtion of fats* from the small intestine.
52. What is the difference between *osmosis* and *diffusion*?
53. Explain the terms *codon, anticodon, regulatory genes* and *operon.*
54. How is the *blood sugar* regulated?
55. Why is *lactic acid* formed during exercise?
56. Explain *gluconeogenesis.*
57. How much energy is released from *palmitic acid* during its complete catabolism?
58. What is *transamination* and what is its importance?
59. How is *urea* formed?
60. Discuss the functions of *thyroxin, glucagon, cortisol* and *somatotrophin.*

Appendix C

The chemical composition of blood and urine — normal values (for an average healthy male of 70kg mass).

Whole blood

Volume	5 - litre
Specific gravity	1,055 - 1,065
pH	7,3 - 7,4
Viscosity (relative)	3 - 6

Cells

Erythrocytes (red blood corpuscles) . . .	4,2 - 4,6 million/μl
Leucocytes (white blood cells)	5 000 - 10 000/μl
Thrombocytes (platelets)	150 000 - 500 000/μl
Percentage of cells (haematocrit) . . .	40 - 48

Plasma — gram/litre

Proteins (total)	70
Albumin	40
Globulins	27
Fibrinogen	3

Non proteins — milligram/litre

Urea	200 - 300 (or 0,2 - 0,3g/l)
Amino acid	350 - 650 (or 0,35 - 0,65g/l)
Bilirubin	2 - 14
Creatine	2 - 9
Creatinine	10 - 20
Uric acid	20 - 60
Glucose	800 - 1 200 (or 0,8 - 1,2g/l)
Citric acid	10 - 30
α-Keto glutaric acid	2 - 10
Lactic acid	80 - 170
Pyruvic acid	4 - 40
Total lipids	2 850 - 6 750 (or 2,85 - 6,75g/l)
Triglycerides	800 - 2 400 (or 0,8 - 2,4g/l)
Cholesterol	1 300 - 2 600 (or 1,3 - 2,6g/l)

	milligram/litre
Total fatty acids	1 500 - 5 000
	(or 1,5 - 5,0g/l)
Iron	0,5 - 1,8
Copper	0,8 - 1,2

Electrolytes

	meq/litre
Total anions	142 - 150
Total cations	142 - 158
Na^+	132 - 150
K^+	3,8 - 5,4
Ca^{++}	4,5 - 5,6
Mg^{++}	1,6 - 2,2
HCO_3^-	24 - 30
Cl^-	100 - 110
$PO_4^=$	1,6 - 2,7
$SO_4^=$	0,7 - 1,5

Urine

Main component: water

Specific gravity	1,001 - 1,040
pH	6,0 - 8,0
	depending upon diet
Volume	1,0 - 1,5/litre/day

Colour: Light to deep yellow due to urochrome

Odour: Not unpleasant

Waste products present

    urea
    uric acid
    creatine
    creatinine
    ammonium ions
    organic sulphates

Excess products present (in varying quantities)

    sodium
    chlorides
    potassium
    calcium
    phosphates
    sulphates

Index